THE EARTH IS THE LORD'S

Poems of the Spirit

THE
EARTH
IS
THE LORD'S

POEMS OF THE SPIRIT

Compiled by Helen Plotz

ILLUSTRATED WITH WOOD ENGRAVINGS
BY CLARE LEIGHTON

THOMAS Y. CROWELL COMPANY

New York

ABELARD-SCHUMAN for "The Angels Came A-Mustering" (Anonymous) and "From Thee to Thee" by Solomon Ibn Gabirol, from *Anthology of Medieval Hebrew Literature* by Abraham E. Millgram, © 1962, reprinted by permission of the publisher.

THE BELKNAP PRESS of Harvard University Press for "Of God We Ask One Favor" by Emily Dickinson, from *The Poems of Emily Dickinson* edited by Thomas H. Johnson, copyright 1951, 1955 by The President and Fellows of Harvard College throughout the world, reprinted by permission of the publishers.

THE BODLEY HEAD LTD. for "To the Sun" by Roy Campbell, from *Collected Poems*, Vol. I.

BRANDT & BRANDT for selections from "John Brown's Body" from *Selected Works of Stephen Vincent Benét*, published by Holt, Rinehart & Winston, copyright 1927, 1928 by Stephen Vincent Benét, copyright renewed © 1955 by Rosemary Carr Benét, reprinted by permission of Brandt & Brandt.

CAMBRIDGE UNIVERSITY PRESS for "Life After Death" by Pindar, from A Book of Greek Verse (1907) edited by Walter Headlam.

JONATHAN CAPE, LTD. for Canadian rights to "Third Enemy Speaks" by C. Day Lewis from *The Magnetic Mountain*; "Son and Father," "Christmas Eve," and "The Great Magicians" by C. Day Lewis from *Pegasus and Other Poems*, copyright 1957.

CHATTO & WINDUS LTD. for Canadian rights to "Chiliasm" by Richard Eberhart from *Undercliff*; "Man Is God's Nature" by Richard Eberhart from *Great Praises*.

THE CLARENDEN PRESS, Oxford, for "Earth and Sky" (Euripides, translated by C. M. Bowra) from *Oxford Book of Greek Verse in Translation* edited by T. G. Higham and C. M. Bowra, reprinted by permission of the publisher.

THE CRESSET PRESS LTD. for "The Sparrow's Skull" by Ruth Pitter from *Urania*; "Father to the Man" by John Knight from *Straight Lines and Unicorns*.

J. M. DENT & SONS LTD. for Canadian rights to "And Death Shall Have No Dominion" by Dylan Thomas from *Collected Poems*, reprinted by permission of the publishers and the Literary Executors of the Dylan Thomas Estate.

DOUBLEDAY & COMPANY, INC. for "In a Dark Time" by Theodore Roethke from *The Far Field*, copyright © 1956 by Kenyon College, reprinted by permission of the publisher.

GERALD DUCKWORTH & CO. LTD. for "Old Shepard's Prayer" by Charlotte Mew from *Collected Poems*.

E. P. DUTTON & CO., Inc. for "Hymn" by Louise Townsend Nicholl from *Collected Poems*, copyright 1941 by E. P. Dutton & Co., Inc., published 1953

By the Author

IMAGINATION'S OTHER PLACE:
Poems of Science and Mathematics

UNTUNE THE SKY:
Poems of Music and the Dance

POEMS OF EMILY DICKINSON

ACKNOWLEDGMENTS

My children have given me encouragement and support, and the younger children, especially, have been of inestimable help. Sarah and John have suggested many poems and have done a good deal of typing, fetching, and carrying. Norma Buckley coped with all the secretarial details.

I cannot list all of the friends who helped in this enterprise and who listened while I talked. They know how much I value their aid.

I should like to express especial thanks to Theresa and Austin Wood.

In memory of

MILTON

INTRODUCTION

In the history of man's long struggle with the idea of God, there has never been a time when he could say "I know." From the earliest days of prehistory, when the fire at the mouth of the cave kept back the dreadful night, to our own age of space exploration, the human condition has been at once uncertain, dangerous, and glorious.

How it came about that men became aware of the mysteries around them, we do not know. Anthropologists and archaeologists have traced the growth of myth, magic, and sacrifice and have dug up altars and idols. And still we cannot tell how men began to look backward to yesterday and forward to tomorrow, to welcome the newborn and to bury their dead, to observe the days and the seasons in their inevitable rhythm. "A something not ourselves" may have been the earliest religious concept grasped by Homo sapiens, "man knowing" — or, perhaps, we should think of him, and of ourselves, as "man questioning."

For we are questioning still. Man's relationship to God and God's to man are the immediate concern of all of us. Man's relationship to his fellowman is bound up with his religious affirmations and with his negations as well. Denial and doubt are inescapable aspects of faith. Countless philosophers have speculated about the nature of God, of the universe, and of man: countless theologians have interpreted God's word. Artists have given order to their own religious aspirations in painting and sculpture, musicians in Mass and oratorio.

And the poets, what of them? Here they are — some serene in their faith, some anguished in their doubt, some unshaken in their unbelief. The ancient symbols of our Judaeo-Christian heritage appear again and again in every age, as the lotus and banyan tree appear in Eastern poetry. The still small voice, the shepherd's crook, the Cross, and the manger are given new meaning for each generation by the poets of that generation. The Massacre of the Innocents and even the Crucifixion are not safely embalmed in the past, where we can think about them or ignore them at our own convenience. They are happening right now. Poets make us see, and they make us hear. They awaken us to compassion or to anger.

The five categories into which I have placed the poems are, like all categories, an arbitrary division of what is essentially indivisible. Nevertheless, there were five themes which appeared again and again.

The first theme is that of man's relationship to God and his endless exploration of God's nature and will. God is unknowable, say the poets, yet they seek always to know Him.

Not all poets nor all prophets have gladly accepted God. Many have fought with Him, doubted His existence, or repudiated Him. And so the second theme is the theme of rebellion and despair. In this section there are poems about God's eternal adversary, Lucifer, the fallen angel, and poems that celebrate man's triumph over doubt.

The third section is devoted to the saints and prophets: God's angry men, some of them, and some of them tranquil and innocent. They loved God fiercely or gently, according to their own natures; yet all loved Him wholly.

We exist in uneasy truce with God's other creatures and in still more uneasy brotherhood with our fellowmen. Sometimes it's easy to rationalize wanton cruelty to "dumb" animals and easier to love God, who is far away, than to love our brothers. But God has required of us that we do justice and love mercy. The brotherhood of man is implicit in the fatherhood of God. Therefore, in this fourth category, there are poems that mourn man's inhumanity to man and to the animals under his dominion. There are poems, too, which joyously proclaim that "He prayeth well who loveth well, Both man and bird and beast."

The last section contains the prayers with which we strive to reach God and the hymns and psalms with which we praise Him. They make a joyful noise unto the Lord. The poets who wrote them have bidden us to come into His presence with gladness. Life is indeed an experiment perilous, yet we may, with the Psalmist, worship the Lord in the beauty of holiness and sing unto Him a new song.

CONTENTS

The Vision Splendid   1
Praise Doubt   63
God's Familiars   95
All Creatures Here Below   119
Our Daily Bread   167
Index of Authors   215
Index of Titles   217
Index of First Lines   220

THE
VISION
SPLENDID

I NEED NO SKY

I need no sky nor stars
When once, beyond the bars
That fence a meadow in,
I have espied a place
Blowing with Queen Anne's lace
Where only stones had been.

New stars have come my way,
Encompassing by day
A constellation's rim;
And, if I dared before
To doubt, I doubt no more
But do believe in Him,

This Hermit who, unknown
To eye or ear, has sown
In a secretive hour,
This Stranger who can make
The whole of heaven wake
And wander in a flower.

WITTER BYNNER

NO COWARD SOUL IS MINE

No coward soul is mine,
No trembler in the world's storm-troubled sphere;
   I see Heaven's glories shine,
And faith shines equal, arming me from fear.

O God within my breast,
Almighty, ever-present Deity!
   Life — that in me has rest,
As I—undying Life—have power in Thee!

   Vain are the thousand creeds
That move men's hearts: unutterably vain;
   Worthless as withered weeds,
Or idle froth amid the boundless main,

   To waken doubt in one
Holding so fast by Thine infinity;
   So surely anchored on
The steadfast rock of immortality.

   With wide-embracing love
Thy spirit animates eternal years
   Pervades and broods above,
Changes, sustains, dissolves, creates, and rears.

   Though earth and man were gone,
And suns and universes ceased to be,
   And Thou were left alone,
Every existence would exist in Thee.

   There is not room for Death,
Nor atom that his might could render void;
   Thou—Thou art Being and Breath
And what Thou art may never be destroyed.

EMILY BRONTË

4

LIFE AFTER DEATH

For them the sun shines ever in full might
Throughout our earthly night;
There, reddening with the rose, their paradise,
A fair green pleasance, lies,
Cool beneath shade of incense-bearing trees,
And rich with golden fruit:
And there they take their pleasure as they will,
In chariot-race, or young-limbed exercise
In wrestling, at the game of tables these,
And those with harp or lute:
And blissful where they dwell, beside them still
Dwells at full bloom perfect felicity:
And spreading delicately
Over the lovely region everywhere
Fragrance in the air
Floats from high altars where the fire is dense
With perfumed frankincense
Burned for the glory of Heaven continually.

PINDAR
Translated by
Walter Headlam

THE YEW-TREE

Is there a cause why we should wake the dead?
Should they not sleep, safe in the sepulchre?
I, a man walking, one alive to fear,
Hear these deep, holy boughs and berries red
Sweep the dark graves, then stop where seem to tread
Long-vanishing mourners from an earlier year.
Late-leaving, then, from each fresh grave I hear
Love's nearmost: 'O, who will lift this lost, loved head,
Crowned with flowers fading, whose quick colors pray?'
Then none makes answer; yet, soon, bodily
Reaching to God, I hear that good thief say:
'Lord, for no wrong Thou diest, but justly we.'
That word kills grief, and through the dark-boughed tree
Gives to each dead his resurrection day.

VERNON WATKINS

THE KINGDOM OF GOD
'In no Strange Land'

O world invisible, we view thee,
O world intangible, we touch thee,
O world unknowable, we know thee,
Inapprehensible, we clutch thee!

Does the fish soar to find the ocean,
The eagle plunge to find the air—
That we ask of the stars in motion
If they have rumour of thee there?

Not where the wheeling systems darken,
And our benumbed conceiving soars!—
The drift of pinions, would we hearken,
Beats at our own clay-shutter'd doors.

The angels keep their ancient places;—
Turn but a stone, and start a wing!
'Tis ye, 'tis your estrangèd faces,
That miss the many-splendour'd thing.

But (when so sad thou canst not sadder)
Cry;—and upon thy so sore loss
Shall shine the traffic of Jacob's ladder
Pitched betwixt Heaven and Charing Cross.

Yea, in the night, my Soul, my daughter,
Cry,—clinging Heaven by the hems;
And lo, Christ walking on the water
Not of Gennesareth, but Thames!

FRANCIS THOMPSON

AT THE GRAVE OF HENRY VAUGHAN

Above the voiceful windings of a river
An old green slab of simply graven stone
Shuns notice, overshadowed by a yew.
Here Vaughan lies dead, whose name flows on for ever
Through pastures of the spirit washed with dew
And starlit with eternities unknown.
Here sleeps the Silurist; the loved physician;
The face that left no portraiture behind;
The skull that housed white angels and had vision
Of daybreak through the gateways of the mind.
　Here faith and mercy, wisdom and humility
　(Whose influence shall prevail for evermore)
　Shine. And this lowly grave tells
　　　　Heaven's tranquillity.
　And here stand I, a suppliant at the door.

SIEGFRIED SASSOON

PEACE

My Soul, there is a Countrie
  Far beyond the stars
Where stands a winged sentrie
  All skillfull in the wars,
There above noise, and danger
  Sweet peace sits crown'd with smiles
And one born in a Manger
  Commands the Beauteous files,
He is thy gracious friend
  And (O my Soul awake!)
Did in pure love descend
  To die here for thy sake,
If thou canst get but thither,
  There growes the flowre of peace,
The Rose that cannot wither,
  Thy fortress, and thy ease;
Leave then thy foolish ranges;
  For none can thee secure,
But one, who never changes,
  Thy God, thy life, thy Cure.

HENRY VAUGHAN

THIS WORLD IS NOT CONCLUSION

This World is not Conclusion.
A Species stands beyond—
Invisible, as Music—
But positive, as Sound—
It beckons, and it baffles—
Philosophy—don't know—
And through a Riddle, at the last—
Sagacity, must go—
To guess it, puzzles scholars—
To gain it, Men have borne
Contempt of Generations
and Crucifixion, shown—
Faith slips—and laughs, and rallies—
Blushes, if any see—
Plucks at a twig of Evidence—
And asks a Vane, the way—
Much Gesture, from the Pulpit—
Strong Hallelujahs roll—
Narcotics cannot still the Tooth
That nibbles at the soul—

EMILY DICKINSON

STONE ANGEL

(On the font in Taynton Church)

I had a beginning but shall have no end:
Even though the blade
Of razing Time
Abrades my form, and though I fade
From memory, stranger, even then
Blazing creatures of my kind
Will cry—Glory to God and peace to men.

ANNE RIDLER

SUNDAY MORNING, KING'S CAMBRIDGE

File into yellow candle light, fair choristers of King's
   Lost in the shadowy silence of canopied Renaissance stalls
In blazing glass above the dark glow skies and thrones and
                                   wings
   Blue, ruby, gold and green between the whiteness of the
                                   walls
And with what rich precision the stonework soars and springs
   To fountain out a spreading vault—a shower that never
                                   falls

The white of windy Cambridge courts, the cobble brown and
                                   dry,
   The gold of plaster Gothic with ivy overgrown,
The apple-red, the silver fronts, the wide green flats and high,
   The yellowing elm-trees circled out on islands of their
                                   own—
Oh, here behold all colors change that catch the flying sky
   To waves of pearly light that heave along the shafted stone.

In far East Anglian churches, the clasped hands lying long
   Recumbent on sepulchral slabs or effigied in brass
Buttress with prayer this vaulted roof so white and light and
                                   strong
   And countless congregations as the generations pass
Join choir and great crowned organ case, in centuries of song
   To praise Eternity contained in Time and coloured glass.

JOHN BETJEMAN

THE OLD GODS

Old gods and goddesses who have lived so long
Through time and never found eternity,
Fettered by wasting wood and hollowing hill,

You should have fled our ever-dying song,
The mound, the well, and the green trysting tree,
They are forgotten, yet you linger still.

Goddess of caverned breast and channelled brow
And cheeks slow hollowed by millenial tears,
Forests of autumns fading in your eyes,

Eternity marvels at your counted years
And kingdoms lost in time, and wonders how
There could be thoughts so bountiful and wise

As yours beneath the ever-breaking bough,
And vast compassion curving like the skies.

EDWIN MUIR

STRANGER

When no one listens
To the quiet trees
When no one notices
The sun in the pool

Where no one feels
The first drop of rain
Or sees the last star

Or hails the first morning
Of a giant world
Where peace begins
And rages end:

One bird sits still
Watching the work of God:
One turning leaf,
Two falling blossoms,
Ten circles upon the pond.

One cloud upon the hillside,
Two shadows in the valley
And the light strikes home.
Now dawn commands the capture
Of the tallest fortune,
The surrender
Of no less marvelous prize!

Closer and clearer
Than any wordy master,
Thou inward Stranger
Whom I have never seen,

Deeper and cleaner
Than the clamorous ocean,
Seize up my silence
Hold me in Thy Hand!

Now act is waste
And suffering undone
Laws become prodigals
Limits are torn down
For envy has no property
And passion is none.

Look, the vast Light stands still
Our cleanest Light is One!

THOMAS MERTON

15

THE GUEST

Yet if his majesty, our Soveraign lord,
Should of his owne accord
Friendly himselfe invite,
And say I'll be your guest tomorrowe night,
How should we stir ourselves, call and command
All hands to worke! 'Let no man idle stand.
Set me fine Spanish tables in the hall,
See they be fitted all;
Let there be roome to eate,
And order taken that there want no meate.
See every sconce and candlestick made bright,
That without tapers they may give a light.
Looke to the presence: are the carpets spred,
The dazie o'er the head,
The cushions in the chayres,
And all the candles lighted on the stairs?
Perfume the chambers, and in any case
Let each man give attendance in his place.'
Thus if a king were coming would we do;
And 'twere good reason too;
For 'tis a duteous thing
To show all honor to an earthly king;
And after all our travayle and our cost,
So he be pleas'd, to think no labour lost.
But at the coming of the King of Heaven
All's set at six and seven:
We wallow in our sin;
Christ cannot finde a chamber in the inn.
We entertaine him alwayes like a stranger,
And, as at first, still lodge him in the manger.

ANONYMOUS
(Possibly by Henry Vaughan)
From a Christ Church ms.

THE COSMIC FABRIC

This vast web, of Nature's weaving,
Is God's garment, so 'tis said.
In that fabric I—a living,
I—a still unbroken thread.
And the thread runs swiftly, never
Halting, yet if once it sever,
Seer or sage shall not suffice
The divided strands to splice.
For the Weaver so will veil it
That (let him who may bewail it)
None the ends shall ever find,
Nor the broken thread rebind.
Ceaselessly the threads are breaking—
Short, ah short will be my span!
Meanwhile at His fabric's making
Toils the cosmic artisan,
Curious patterns still designing,
Wave and crested hill defining,
Steppe and pasture, cloud and sky,
Wood and field of golden rye.
Vainly may the wise men scan it:
Flawless since that Hand began it,
Smooth and fine, with beauty stored,
Shines the garment of the Lord!

YAKOV POLONSKY

THE LAMB

Little Lamb, who made thee?
　Dost thou know who made thee?
Gave thee life, and bid thee feed,
By the stream and o'er the mead;
Gave thee clothing of delight,
Softest clothing, woolly, bright;
Gave thee such a tender voice,
Making all the vales rejoice?
　Little Lamb, who made thee?
　Dost thou know who made thee?

Little Lamb, I'll tell thee,
　Little Lamb, I'll tell thee:
He is callèd by thy name,
For He calls Himself a Lamb.
He is meek, and He is mild;
He became a little child.
I a child, and thou a lamb,
We are callèd by His name.
　Little Lamb, God bless thee!
　Little Lamb, God bless thee!

WILLIAM BLAKE

THE TYGER

Tyger! Tyger! burning bright
In the forests of the night,
What immortal hand or eye
Could frame thy fearful symmetry?

In what distant deeps or skies
Burnt the fire of thine eyes?
On what wings dare he aspire?
What the hand dare seize the fire?

And what shoulder, and what art,
Could twist the sinews of thy heart?
And when thy heart began to beat,
What dread hand? and what dread feet?

What the hammer? what the chain?
In what furnace was thy brain?
What the anvil? what dread grasp
Dare its deadly terrors clasp?

When the stars threw down their spears,
And water'd heaven with their tears,
Did He smile His work to see?
Did He who made the Lamb make thee?

Tyger! Tyger! burning bright
In the forests of the night,
What immortal hand or eye,
Dare frame thy fearful symmetry?

WILLIAM BLAKE

THEOLOGIANS

They argued on till dead of night—
' "God" ' versus ' "God" '—till
ceased to shine
The stars in cold Olympus: and
Daybreak their very faces proved divine!

WALTER DE LA MARE

TO THE SUN

Oh let your shining orb grow dim,
Of Christ the mirror and the shield,
That I may gaze through you to Him,
See half the miracle revealed,
And in your seven hues behold
The Blue Man walking on the Sea;
The Green, beneath the summer tree,
Who called the children; then the Gold
With palms; the Orange, flaring bold
With scourges; Purple in the garden
(As Greco saw): and then the Red
Torero (Him who took the toss
And rode the black horns of the cross—
But rose snow-silver from the dead!)

ROY CAMPBELL
From
"Mithraic Emblems"

THE ZEN ARCHER

For the second shot,
Rattling his stiff paper robes
He turns his shoulder to
The festive target, that is nothing,
With ceremonious ease
Lays fingers on the string
And lifts the bow above his head.

Moving his hands apart,
He brings the arrow to his level eye.
In one gesture, or lack of it,
Indifferent, formal, bold,
Lets fly the shaft that is
Himself, and splits
The first arrow at the centre of the gold.

JAMES KIRKUP

BRAHMA

If the red slayer think he slays,
    Of if the slain think he is slain,
They know not well the subtle ways
    I keep, and pass, and turn again.

Far or forgot to me is near;
    Shadow and sunlight are the same;
The vanish'd gods to me appear;
    And one to me are shame and fame.

They reckon ill who leave me out;
    When me they fly, I am the wings;
I am the doubter and the doubt,
    And I the hymn the Brahmin sings.

The strong gods pine for my abode,
    And pine in vain the sacred Seven;
But thou, meek lover of the good!
    Find me, and turn thy back on heaven.

RALPH WALDO EMERSON

HE IS LIKE THE LOTUS

I am the pure lotus,
Springing up in splendor
Fed by the breath of Ra.

Rising into sunlight,
Out of soil and darkness,
I blossom in the Field.

From the
Book of the Dead
Translated by
Robert Hillyer

THE GIVER OF LIFE

The Giver of Life
Placed the sun in great space,
And said: No hand
Shall be the length to reach it;
Though clouds disappear,
And we become a mountain
Immovable and high,
It will not be that the hand obeys not.

The Giver of Life
Placed the sun in the heavens,
And said: No eye
Shall have the cunning to see within,
Though clouds disappear,
And we become a mountain
Invisible and high,
It will not be that the eye obeys not.

DAHOMEAN SONG

Translated by
Frances Herskovits

JOURNEY OF THE MAGI

'A cold coming we had of it,
Just the worst time of the year
For a journey, and such a long journey:
The ways deep and the weather sharp,
The very dead of winter.'
And the camels galled, sore-footed, refractory,
Lying down in the melting snow.
There were times we regretted
The summer palaces on slopes, the terraces,
And the silken girls bringing sherbet.
Then the camel men cursing and grumbling
And running away, and wanting their liquor and women,
And the night-fires going out, and the lack of shelters,
And the cities hostile and the towns unfriendly
And the villages dirty and charging high prices:
A hard time we had of it.
At the end we preferred to travel all night,
Sleeping in snatches,
With the voices singing in our ears, saying
That this was all folly.

    Then at dawn we came to a temperate valley,
Wet, below the snow line, smelling of vegetation;
With a running stream and a water-mill beating the darkness,
And three trees on the low sky,
And an old white horse galloped away in the meadow.
Then we came to a tavern with vine-leaves over the lintel,
Six hands at an open door dicing for pieces of silver,
And feet kicking the empty wine-skins.
But there was no information, and so we continued
And arrived at evening, not a moment too soon
Finding the place; it was (you may say) satisfactory.

All this was a long time ago, I remember,
And I would do it again, but set down
This set down
This: were we led all that way for
Birth or Death? There was a Birth, certainly,
We had evidence and no doubt. I had seen birth and death,
But had thought they were different; this Birth was
Hard and bitter agony for us, like Death, our death.
We returned to our places, these Kingdoms,
But no longer at ease here, in the old dispensation,
With an alien people clutching their gods.
I should be glad of another death.

T. S. ELIOT

THE SECOND COMING

Turning and turning in the widening gyre
The falcon cannot hear the falconer;
Things fall apart; the centre cannot hold;
Mere anarchy is loosed upon the world,
The blood-dimmed tide is loosed, and everywhere
The ceremony of innocence is drowned;
The best lack all conviction, while the worst
Are full of passionate intensity.

Surely some revelation is at hand;
Surely the Second Coming is at hand.
The Second Coming! Hardly are those words out
When a vast image out of *Spiritus Mundi*
Troubles my sight: somewhere in sands of the desert
A shape with lion body and the head of a man,
A gaze blank and pitiless as the sun,
Is moving its slow thighs, while all about it
Reel shadows of the indignant desert birds.
The darkness drops again; but now I know
That twenty centuries of stony sleep
Were vexed to nightmare by a rocking cradle,
And what rough beast, its hour come round at last,
Slouches towards Bethlehem to be born?

WILLIAM BUTLER YEATS

CHRISTMAS EVE

Come out for a while and look from the outside in
At a room you know
As the firelight fitfully beats on the windowpane—
An old heart sinking low,
And the whispering melting kisses of the snow
Soothe time from your brow.

It is Christmastide. Does the festival promise as fairly
As ever to you? 'I feel
The numbness of one whose drifted years conceal
His original landmarks of good and ill.
For a heart weighed down by its own and the
                                world's folly
This season has little appeal.'

But tomorrow is Christmas Day. Can it really mean
Nothing to you? 'It is hard
To see it as more than a time-worn, tinsel routine,
Or else a night incredibly starred,
Angels, oxen, A Babe—the recurrent dream
Of a Christmas card.'

You must try again. Say 'Christmas Eve.' Now, quick,
What do you see?
'I see in the firelit room a child is awake,
Mute with expectancy
For the berried day, the presents, the Christmas cake,
Is he mine? or me?'

He is you, and yours. Desiring for him tomorrow's
Feast—the crackers, the Tree, the piled
Presents—you lose your self in his yearning,
                                and borrow

His eyes to behold
Your own young world again. Love's mystery is revealed
When the father becomes the child.

'Yet would it not make those carolling angels weep
To think how incarnate Love
Means such trivial joys to us children of unbelief?'
No. It's a miracle great enough
If through centuries, clouded and dingy, this Day
                                can keep

Expectation alive.

C. DAY LEWIS

JESUS AND HIS MOTHER

My only son, more God's than mine,
Stay in this garden ripe with pears.
The yielding of their substance wears
A modest and contented shine:
And when they weep with age, not brine
But lazy syrup are their tears.
'I am my own and not my own.'

He seemed much like another man,
That silent foreigner who trod
Outside my door with lily rod:
How could I know what I began
Meeting the eyes more furious than
The eyes of Joseph, those of God?
I was my own and not my own.

And who are these twelve labouring men?
I do not understand your words:
I taught you speech, we named the birds,
You marked their big migration then
Like any child. So turn again
To silence from the place of crowds.
'I am my own and not my own.'

Why are you sullen when I speak?
Here are your tools, the saw and knife
And hammer on your bench. Your life
Is measured here in week and week
Planed as the furniture you make,
And I will teach you like a wife
To be my own and all my own.

Who like an arrogant wind blown
Where he may please, needs no content?
Yet I remember how you went
To speak with scholars in furred gown.
I hear an outcry in the town;
Who carried that dark instrument?
'One all his own and not his own.'

Treading the green and nimble sward,
I stare at a strange shadow thrown.
Are you the boy I bore alone,
No doctor near to cut the cord?
I cannot reach to call you Lord,
Answer me as my only son.
'I am my own and not my own.'

THOM GUNN

FATHER TO THE MAN

I warned the parents, you know,
when he was a child. I said

This boy must really not be allowed
to argue about law with lawyers and about God
with theologians. And he seems, I said,
to fancy himself as a doctor, too. At this rate
we shall have him, perhaps, giving water
to a feverish patient. Little thinking
he'd do just that; and was lucky
the lad recovered.

It will come to no good, I said.
But one gets no thanks.

And so it went on
until, later, we lost touch;
for he was away for some years,
no one knew where.

Afterwards, I admit, I was half convinced. More than half,
I suppose I should say.

When he preached—and I shall hear no such sermons again—
it seemed that immutable right and wrong—
no, it was not that their boundaries changed, but somehow
acts and facts seemed with a shake of a word
to fall—I saw such a toy once, of foolish beads—
in a different pattern. What was done was the same,
and right and wrong were the same, and yet
not the same, being done in a different world.

There was a wedding, for instance,
with, in plain Aramaic, too much drink,

and you know the country customs—
I fear the old Gods are by no means dead.
Well, he was there, and he preached on the sabbath,
and spoke, just in passing, about the wedding;
and, you know, these junketings (to call them no worse)
seemed transformed, seemed a part
(like David's dancing in the Temple)
of our holy religion; and,
what is stranger, our religion
seemed to have grown, and to be our life.

Well, you see, it has come to no good,
as I told his parents, children
must listen, and lawful authority speak.

. . . and yet
    this is the saddest news . . . and I
    am nearer to death . . .

JOHN KNIGHT

BUT GOD'S OWN DESCENT

But God's own descent
Into flesh was meant
As a demonstration
That the supreme merit
Lay in risking spirit
In substantiation.

Spirit enters flesh
And for all it's worth
Charges into earth
In birth after birth
Ever fresh and fresh.
We may take the view
That its derring-do
Thought of in the large
Is one mighty charge
On our human part
Of the soul's ethereal
Into the material.

ROBERT FROST
From
"Kitty Hawk"

SEVEN STANZAS AT EASTER

Make no mistake: if He rose at all
it was as His body;
if the cells' dissolution did not reverse, the molecules
            reknit, the amino acids rekindle
the Church will fall.

It was not as the flowers,
each soft Spring recurrent;
it was not as His Spirit in the mouths and fuddled
            eyes of the eleven apostles;
it was as His flesh: ours.

The same hinged thumbs and toes,
the same valved heart
that—pierced—died, withered, paused, and then
          regathered out of enduring Might
new strength to enclose.

Let us not mock God with metaphor,
analogy, sidestepping, transcendence;
making of the event a parable, a sign painted in the
            faded credulity of earlier ages:
let us walk through the door.

The stone is rolled back, not pâpier-maché,
not a stone in a story,
but the vast rock of materiality that in the slow grinding of
            time will eclipse for each of us
the wide light of day.

And if we will have an angel at the tomb,
make it a real angel,
weighty with Max Planck's quanta, vivid with hair, opaque in
                            the dawn light, robed in real linen
spun on a definite loom.

Let us not seek to make it less monstrous,
for our own convenience, our own sense of beauty,
lest, awakened in one unthinkable hour, we are embarrassed
                                   by the miracle
and crushed by remonstrance.

JOHN UPDIKE

FORGIVENESS

What shall we say it is to be forgiven?—
 To be in Heaven?
Is it to be released?
 A darkness lighted?
Something of this at least,
 But more, the marriage-feast.
To be forgiven is to be invited.

What shall we say it is to be forgiven?—
 To be in Heaven?
To see three rainbows in an hour,
 That every shower
Shone as it rained?
Here was some insight gained.
To be forgiven is to be explained.

What shall we say it is to be forgiven?—
 To be in Heaven?
To gaze at moon-washed trees
 Before we slept?
 A hint from these.
It is a 'yes' that wept,
But not to be accepted: to accept.

What shall we say it is to be forgiven?—
 To be in Heaven?
 Is it to meet
A well-beloved on an alien street,
 Sudden and unexpected?
 Perhaps connected.
To be forgiven: to be re-directed.

What shall we say it is to be forgiven?—
    To be in Heaven?
  To see, distant but clear,
    The Promised Land?
  Is it Jerusalem and Samarcand?
    More near.
To be forgiven is to understand.

ELIZABETH SEWELL

OH THOU,
WHO MAN OF BASER EARTH
DIDST MAKE

Oh Thou, who Man of baser Earth didst make,
And even with Paradise devise the Snake:
For all the Sin wherewith the Face of Man
Is blackened—Man's forgiveness give—and take!

From
"The Rubáiyát of Omar Khayyám"
Translated by
Edward Fitzgerald

FORGIVE, O LORD,
MY LITTLE JOKES
ON THEE

Forgive, O Lord, my little jokes on Thee
And I'll forgive Thy great big one on me.

ROBERT FROST

THE CREDITOR

The quietude of a soft wind
Will not rescind
My debts to God, but gentle-skinned
His finger probes. I lull myself
In quiet in diet in riot in dreams,
In dopes in drams in drums in dreams
Till God retire and the door shut.
But
Now I am left in the fire-blaze
The peacefulness of the fire-blaze
Will not erase
My debts to God for His mind strays
Over and under and all ways
All days and always.

LOUIS MAC NEICE

THIRD ENEMY SPEAKS

God is a proposition,
And we that prove him are his priests, his chosen.
From bare hypothesis
Of strata and wind, of stars and tides, watch me
Construct his universe,
A working model of my majestic notions,
A sum done in the head.
Last week I measured the light, his little finger;
The rest is a matter of time.

God is an electrician,
And they that worship him must worship him
In ampere and in volt.
Scrap sun and moon, your twilight of false gods;
X. is not here or there;
Whose lightning scrawls brief cryptograms on sky,
Easy for us to solve;
Whose motions fit our formulae, whose temple
Is a pure apparatus.

God is a statistician:
Offer him all the data; tell him your dreams.
What is your lucky number?
How do you react to bombs? Have you a rival?
Do you really love your wife?
Get yourself taped. Put soul upon the table:
Switch on the arc-lights; watch
Heart's beat, the secret agents of the blood.
Let every cell be observed.

God is a Good Physician,
Gives fruit for hygiene, crops for calories.
Don't touch that dirty man,

Don't drink from the same cup, sleep in one bed:
You know He would not like it.
Young men, cut out those visions, they're bad
                                    for the eyes:
I'll show you face to face
Eugenics, Eupeptics and Euthanasia,
The clinic Trinity.

                                    C. DAY LEWIS

REDEMPTION

Having been tenant long to a rich Lord,
   Not thriving, I resolved to be bold,
   And make a suit unto him, to afford
A new small-rented lease, and cancell th'old.

In heaven at his manor I him sought:
   They told me there, that he was lately gone
   About some land, which he had dearly bought
Long since on earth, to take possession.

I straight return'd, and knowing his great birth,
   Sought him accordingly in great resorts;
   In cities, theatres, gardens, parks, and courts:
At length I heard a ragged noise and mirth

   Of theeves and murderers: there I him espied,
Who straight, *Your suit is granted*, said, and died.

GEORGE HERBERT

THE PROOF

Shall I love God for causing me to be?
I was mere utterance; shall these words love me?

Yet when I caused his work to jar and stammer,
And one free subject loosened all his grammar,

I love him that he did not in a rage,
Once and forever rule me off the page,

But, thinking I might come to please him yet,
Crossed out *delete* and wrote his patient *stet*.

RICHARD WILBUR

IN A DARK TIME

In a dark time, the eye begins to see,
I meet my shadow in the deepening shade;
I hear my echo in the echoing wood—
A lord of nature weeping to a tree.
I live between the heron and the wren,
Beasts of the hill and serpents of the den.

What's madness but nobility of soul
At odds with circumstances? The day's on fire!
I know the purity of pure despair,
My shadow pinned against a sweating wall.
That place among the rocks—is it a cave,
Or winding path? The edge is what I have.

A steady storm of correspondences!
A night flowing with birds, a ragged moon,
And in broad day the midnight come again!
A man goes far to find out what he is—
Death of the self in a long, tearless night,
All natural shapes blazing unnatural light.

Dark, dark my light, and darker my desire.
My soul, like some heat-maddened summer fly,
Keeps buzzing at the sill. Which I is *I*?
A fallen man, I climb out of my fear.
The mind enters self, and God the mind,
And one is One, free in the tearing wind.

THEODORE ROETHKE

GIVING AND TAKING

Take as a gift
A love all freely given.
A great Lord commends your thrift.
Keep as His gift
This hope of heaven.

To take is hard
For minds narrowed by living.
But open your breath to a word.
To take is hard,
When it is giving.

Let breath increase
Within your heart and spirit
Your gain is His, His gain your lease
Of breath's increase
That gives life credit.

Faith is His Bond
Love's capital assures.
Such grace does more than lend.
Faith is your bond.
Give. It is yours.

Give as a gift
A love all freely given.
A great word reveals its drift.
Treasure the gift
Of spendthrift heaven.

JAMES KIRKUP

47

FROM THEE TO THEE

When all within is dark,
    And former friends misprise;
From them I turn to Thee,
    And find Love in Thine eyes.

When all within is dark,
    And I my soul despise;
From me I turn to Thee,
    And find Love in Thine eyes.

When all Thy face is dark,
    And Thy just angers rise;
From Thee I turn to Thee,
    And find Love in Thine eyes.

SOLOMON IBN GABIROL
Translated by
Israel Abrahams

HUSWIFERY

Make me thy Spinning Wheele of use for thee,
   Thy Grace my Distaffe, and my heart thy Spoole.
Turn thou the wheele: let mine Affections bee
   The flyer filling with thy yarne my soule.
   Then weave the web of Grace in mee, thy Loome
   And Cloath my soule therewith, its Glories bloome.

Make me thy Loome: thy Grace the warfe therein,
   My duties Woofe, and let thy word winde Quills.
The shuttle shoot. Cut off the ends my sins.
   Thy Ordinances make my fulling mills,
   My Life thy Web: and cloath me all my dayes
   With this Gold-web of Glory to thy praise.

EDWARD TAYLOR

MY, FELLOWSHIP, WITH, GOD

My, Fellowship, with, God—
My, University. Degree?
None. His, Fellows, go,
Unalphabeted.

JOSÉ GARCIA VILLA

GOD, IS, LIKE, SCISSORS

God, is, like, scissors,
Always, a, pair,
He, there, me, here.

JOSÉ GARCIA VILLA

THE PULLEY

When God at first made man,
Having a glasse of blessings standing by;
Let us (said he) poure on him all we can;
Let the world's riches, which dispersed lie,
    Contract into a span.

So strength first made a way;
Then beautie flow'd, then wisdome, honour, pleasure:
When almost all was out, God made a stay,
Perceiving that alone of all his treasure
    Rest in the bottome lay.

For if I should (said he)
Bestow this jewell also on my creature,
He would adore my gifts in stead of me,
And rest in Nature, not the God of Nature:
    So both should losers be.

Yet let him keep the rest,
But keep them with repining restlesnesse:
Let him be rich and wearie, that at least,
If goodness leade him not, yet wearinesse
    May tosse him to my breast.

GEORGE HERBERT

BATTER MY HEART,
THREE PERSON'D GOD

Batter my heart, three person'd God; for, you
As yet but knocke, breathe, shine, and seeke to mend;
That I may rise, and stand, o'erthrow mee, 'and bend
Your force, to breake, blowe, burn and make me new.
I, like an usurpt towne, to 'another due,
Labour to 'admit you, but Oh, to no end,
Reason your viceroy in mee, mee should defend,
But is captiv'd, and proves weake or untrue.
Yet dearely 'I love you,' and would be loved faine,
But am bethroth'd unto your enemie:
Divorce mee, 'untie, or breake that knot againe,
Take mee to you, imprison mee, for I
Except you' enthrall mee, never shall be free,
Nor ever chast, except you ravish mee.

JOHN DONNE

POOR SOUL, THE CENTER OF MY SINFUL EARTH

Poor soul, the center of my sinful earth,
Rebuke these rebel powers that thee array!
Why dost thou pine within and suffer dearth
Painting thy outward walls so costly gay?
Why so large cost, having so short a lease,
Dost thou upon thy fading mansion spend?
Shall worms, inheritors of this excess,
Eat up thy charge? Is this thy body's end?
Then, soul, live thou upon thy servant's loss,
And let that pine to aggravate thy store;
Buy terms divine in selling hours of dross:
Within be fed, without be rich no more.
So shalt thou feed on Death, that feeds on men,
And Death once dead, there's no more dying then.

WILLIAM SHAKESPEARE

THE WAY MY IDEAS THINK ME

The way my ideas think me
Is the way I unthink God.
As in the name of heaven I make hell
That is the way the Lord says me.

And all is adventure and danger
And I roll Him off cliffs and mountains
But fast as I am to push Him off
Fast am I to reach Him below.

And it may be then His turn to push me off,
I wait breathless for that terrible second:
And if He push me not, I turn around in anger:
"O art *thou* the God I would have!"

Then he pushes me and I plunge down, down!
And when He comes to help me up
I put my arms around Him, saying, "Brother,
Brother." . . . This is the way we are.

JOSÉ GARCIA VILLA

WHAT WILL YOU DO, GOD,
WHEN I DIE?

What will you do, God, when I die?
When I, your pitcher, shattered lie?
When I, your drink, go stale or dry?
I am your garb, the trade you ply,
you lose your meaning, losing me.

Homeless without me, you will be
robbed of your welcome, warm and sweet.
I am your sandals: your tired feet
will wander bare for want of me.

Your mighty cloak will fall away.
Your glance that on my cheek was laid
and pillowed warm, will seek, dismayed,
the comfort that I offered once—
to lie, as sunset colors fade
in the cold lap of alien stones.

What will you do, God? I am afraid.

RAINER MARIA RILKE
Translated by
Babette Deutsch

WE ARE ALL WORKMEN

We are all workmen: prentice, journeyman,
or master, building you—you towering nave.
and sometimes there will come to us a grave
wayfarer, who like a radiance thrills
the souls of all the hundred artisans,
as tremblingly he shows us a new skill.

We climb up on the rocking scaffolding,
the hammers in our hands swing heavily,
until our foreheads feel the caressing wing
of a bright hour that knows everything,
and hails from you as wind hails from the sea.

Then hammerstrokes sound, multitudinous,
and through the mountains echoes blast on blast.
Only at dusk we yield you up at last:
and slow your shaping contours dawn on us.

God, you are vast.

RAINER MARIA RILKE
Translated by
Babette Deutsch

THE BURNING BUSH

When Moses, musing in the desert, found
The thorn bush spiking up from the hot ground,
And saw the branches on a sudden bear
The crackling yellow barberries of fire,

He searched his learning and imagination
For any logical, neat explanation,
And turned to go, but turned again and stayed
And faced the fire and knew it for his God.

I too have seen the briar alight like coal,
The love that burns, the flesh that's ever whole,
And many times have turned and left it there,
Saying: 'It's prophecy—but metaphor.'

But stinging tongues like John the Baptist shout:
'That this is metaphor is no way out.
It's dogma too, or you make God a liar;
The bush is still a bush, and fire is fire.'

NORMAN NICHOLSON

AT THE ROUND EARTH'S
IMAGIN'D CORNERS, BLOW

At the round earths imagin'd corners, blow
Your trumpets, Angells, and arise, arise
From death, you numberlesse infinities
Of soules, and to your scattred bodies goe,
All whom the flood did, and fire shall o'erthrow,
All whom warre, dearth, age, agues, tyrannies,
Despaire, law, chance, hath slaine, and you whose eyes.
Shall behold God, and never taste deaths woe.
But let them sleepe, Lord, and mee mourne a space,
For, if above all these, my sinnes abound,
'Tis late to aske abundance of thy grace,
When wee are there; here on this lowly ground,
Teach mee how to repent; for that's as good
As thou hadst seal'd my pardon, with thy blood.

JOHN DONNE

OUR BIRTH IS BUT A SLEEP
AND A FORGETTING

Our birth is but a sleep and a forgetting:
The Soul that rises with us, our life's Star,
    Hath had elsewhere its setting,
    And cometh from afar:
    Not in entire forgetfulness,
    And not in utter nakedness,
But trailing clouds of glory do we come
    From God, who is our home:
Heaven lies about us in our infancy!
Shades of the prison-house begin to close
    Upon the growing Boy.
But he beholds the light, and whence it flows,
    He sees it in his joy;
The Youth, who daily farther from the east
    Must travel, still is Nature's Priest,
    And by the vision splendid
    Is on his way attended;
At length the Man perceives it die away,
And fade into the light of common day.

WILLIAM WORDSWORTH
From
"Ode: Intimations of Immortality
from Recollections of Early
Childhood"

AND DEATH SHALL HAVE
NO DOMINION

And death shall have no dominion.
Dead men naked they shall be one
With the man in the wind and the west moon;
When their bones are picked clean and the clean bones gone,
They shall have stars at elbow and foot;
Though they go mad they shall be sane,
Though they sink through the sea they shall rise again;
Though lovers be lost love shall not;
And death shall have no dominion.

And death shall have no dominion.
Under the windings of the sea
They lying long shall not die windily;
Twisting on racks when sinews give way,
Strapped to a wheel, yet they shall not break;
Faith in their hands shall snap in two,
And the unicorn evils run them through;
Split all ends up they shan't crack;
And death shall have no dominion.

And death shall have no dominion.
No more may gulls cry at their ears
Or waves break loud on the seashores;
Where blew a flower may a flower no more
Lift its head to the blows of the rain;
Though he be mad and dead as nails,
Heads of the characters hammer through daisies;
Break in the sun till the sun breaks down,
And death shall have no dominion.

DYLAN THOMAS

HE IS THE WAY

He is the Way.
Follow Him through the Land of Unlikeness;
You will see rare beasts, and have unique
      adventures.

He is the Truth.
Seek Him in the Kingdom of Anxiety;
You will come to a great city that has
      expected your return for years.

He is the Life.
Love Him in the World of the Flesh;
And at your marriage all its occasions
      shall dance for joy.

W. H. AUDEN
From
"For the Time Being: A
Christmas Oratorio"

PRAISE
DOUBT

HAP

If but some vengeful god would call to me
From up the sky, and laugh: 'Thou suffering thing,
Know that thy sorrow is my ecstacy,
That thy love's loss is my hate's profiting!'

Then would I bear it, clench myself, and die,
Steeled by the sense of ire unmerited;
Half-eased in that a Powerfuller than I
Had willed and meted me the tears I shed.

But not so. How arrives it joy lies slain,
And why unblooms the best hope ever sown?
—Crass Casualty obstructs the sun and rain,
And dicing Time for gladness casts a moan. . . .
These purblind Doomsters had as readily strown
Blisses about my pilgrimage as pain.

THOMAS HARDY

MYSELF WHEN YOUNG
DID EAGERLY FREQUENT

Myself when young did eagerly frequent
Doctor and Saint, and heard great argument
   About it and about: but evermore
Came out by the same door where in I went.

With them the seed of Wisdom did I sow,
And with mine own hand wrought to make it grow;
   And this was all the Harvest that I reaped—
'I came like Water, and like Wind I go.'

We are no other than a moving row
Of Magic Shadow-shapes that come and go
   Round with the Sun-illumined Lantern held
In Midnight by the Master of the Show;

But helpless Pieces of the Game He plays
Upon this Checker-board of Nights and Days;
   Hither and thither moves, and checks, and slays,
And one by one back in the Closet lays.

From
"The Rubáiyát of Omar Khayyám"
Translated by
Edward Fitzgerald

MY SOUL IS WEARY OF MY LIFE

1   My soul is weary of my life; I will leave my complaint upon myself; I will speak in the bitterness of my soul.

2   I will say unto God, Do not condemn me; show me wherefore thou contendest with me.

3   Is it good unto thee that thou shouldest oppress, that thou shouldest despise the work of thine hands, and shine upon the counsel of the wicked?

4   Hast thou eyes of flesh? or seest thou as man seeth?

5   Are thy days as the days of man? are thy years as man's days,

6   That thou inquirest after mine iniquity, and searchest after my sin?

7   Thou knowest that I am not wicked; and there is none that can deliver out of thine hand.

8   Thine hands have made me and fashioned me together round about; yet thou dost destroy me.

9   Remember, I beseech thee, that thou has made me as the clay; and wilt thou bring me into dust again?

10   Hast thou not poured me out as milk, and curdled me like cheese?

11   Thou hast clothed me with skin and flesh, and hast fenced me with bones and sinews.

12   Thou hast granted me life and favor, and thy visitation hath preserved my spirit.

13   And these things hast thou hid in thine heart: I know that this is with thee.

14   If I sin, then thou markest me, and thou wilt not acquit me from mine iniquity.

15   If I be wicked, woe unto me; and if I be righteous, yet will I not lift up my head. I am full of confusion; therefore see thou mine affliction;

16   For it increaseth. Thou huntest me as a fierce lion: and again thou showest thyself marvellous upon me.

17 Thou renewest thy witnesses against me, and increasest thine indignation upon me; changes and war are against me.

18 Wherefore then hast thou brought me forth out of the womb? Oh that I had given up the ghost, and no eye had seen me!

19 I should have been as though I had not been; I should have been carried from the womb to the grave.

20 Are not my days few? cease then, and let me alone, that I may take comfort a little.

21 Before I go whence I shall not return, even to the land of darkness and the shadow of death;

22 A land of darkness, as darkness itself; and of the shadow of death, without any order, and where the light is as darkness.

JOB 10

CURSE GOD AND DIE,
YOU SAID TO ME

J. B.: Curse God and die, you said to me.
SARAH: Yes.

*She looks up at him for the first time, then down
again.*

You wanted justice, didn't you?
There isn't any. That's the world . . .

*She begins to rock on the doorsill, the little branch
in her arms.*

Cry for justice and the stars
Will stare until your eyes sting. Weep,
Enormous winds will thrash the water.
Cry in sleep for your lost children,
Snow will fall . . .
            snow will fall . . .
J. B.: Why did you leave me alone?
SARAH: I loved you.
I couldn't help you any more.
You wanted justice and there was none—
Only love.
J. B.: He does not love. He Is.
SARAH: But we do. That's the wonder.

ARCHIBALD MAC LEISH
From
"J. B."

THERE ARE NO GODS

Doth some one say that there be gods above?
There are not; no, there are not. Let no fool,
Led by the old false fable, thus deceive you.
Look at the facts themselves, yielding my words
No undue credence: for I say that kings
Kill, rob, break oaths, lay cities waste by fraud,
And doing thus are happier than those
Who live calm pious lives day after day.
How many little States that serve the gods
Are subject to the godless but more strong,
Made slaves by might of a superior army!
And you, if any ceased from work and prayed
To gods, nor gathered in his livelihood,
Would learn gods are not. All Divinity
Is built up from our good and evil luck.

EURIPIDES
Translated by
J. A. Symonds

OF GOD WE ASK ONE FAVOR

Of God we ask one favor,
That we may be forgiven—
For what, he is presumed to know—
The Crime, from us, is hidden—
Immured the whole of Life
Within a magic Prison
We reprimand the Happiness
That too competes with Heaven.

EMILY DICKINSON

THERE WAS ONE I MET
UPON THE ROAD

There was one I met upon the road
Who looked at me with kind eyes.
He said: "Show me of your wares."
And I did,
Holding forth one.
He said: "It is a sin."
Then I held forth another.
He said: "It is a sin."
Then I held forth another.
He said: "It is a sin."
And so to the end.
Always He said: "It is a sin."
At last, I cried out:
"But I have none other."
He looked at me
With kinder eyes.
"Poor soul," He said.

STEPHEN CRANE

ANTICHRIST

He walks, the enchanter, on his sea of glass,
Poring upon his blue inverted heaven
Where a false sun revolves from west to east.
If he could raise his eyes he would see his hell.
In him all is reversed; evil is good.

72

He is no spirit, nor a spirit's shadow,
But a mere toy shaped by ingenious devils
To bring discomfiture on credulous man.
He's the false copy where each feature's wrong,
Yet so disposed the whole gives a resemblance,
The perfect image of his opposite.
When he's in anguish smiles writhe on his lips
And will not stop; his imperturbable brow
Is carved by rage not his but theirs that made him,
For he's a nothing where they move in freedom,
Knowing that nothing's there. When he forgives
It is for love of sin, not of the sinner.
He takes sin for his province, knows sin only,
Nothing but sin from end to end of the world.
He heals the sick to show his conjuring skill,
Vexed only by the cure; and turns his cheek
To goad the furious to more deadly fury
And damn by a juggling trick the ingenuous sinner.
He brings men from the dead to show the living
That their undoing is a common fetch.
Ingeniously he postures on the Tree
(His crowning jest), an actor miming death,
While his indifferent mind is idly pleased
That treason should run on through time for ever.
His vast indulgence is so free and ample
You well might think it universal love,
For all seems goodness, sweetness, harmony.
He is the Lie: one true thought, and he's gone.

EDWIN   MUIR

AFTER READING CERTAIN BOOKS

It's a great deal better to lose than win,
And virtue is nothing compared to sin,
And to get out of Heaven's the way to get in,
   Said the Devil.

For the narrow way, as we know full well,
Is the way that leads a saint to Hell,
And who can rise that never fell?
   Said the Devil.

And if God forgave, not when you would,
But whenever you did the best you could,
What room would there be for God to be good?
   Said the Devil.

MARY COLERIDGE

LUCIFER IN THE TRAIN

Riding the black express from heaven to hell
He bit his fingers, watched the countryside,
Vernal and crystalline, forever slide
Beyond his gaze: the long cascades that fell
Ribboned in sunshine from their sparkling height,
The fishers fastened to their pools of green
By silver lines; the birds in sudden flight—
All things the diabolic eye had seen
Since heaven's cockcrow. Imperceptibly
That landscape altered: now in paler air
Tree, hill and rock stood out resigned, severe,
Beside the strangled field, the stream run dry.

Lucifer, we are yours who stiff and mute
Ride out of worlds we shall not see again,
And watch from windows of a smoking train
The ashen prairies of the absolute.
Once out of heaven, to an angel's eye
Where is the bush or cloud without a flaw?
What bird but feeds upon mortality,
Flies to its young with carrion in its claw?
O foundered angel, first and loneliest
To turn this bitter sand beneath your hoe,
Teach us, the newly-landed, what you know;
After our weary transit, find us rest.

ADRIENNE CECILE RICH

WHAT THOUGH THE FIELD BE LOST?

What though the field be lost?
All is not lost—the unconquerable will,
And study of revenge, immortal hate,
And courage never to submit or yield:
And what is else not to be overcome?
That glory never shall his wrath or might
Extort from me. To bow and sue for grace
With suppliant knee, and deify his power
Who, from the terror of this arm, so late
Doubted his empire—that were low indeed;
That were an ignominy and shame beneath
This downfall; since, by fate, the strength of Gods,
And this empyreal substance, cannot fail;
Since, through experience of this great event,
In arms not worse, in foresight much advanced,
We may with more successful hope resolve
To wage by force or guile eternal war,
Irreconcilable to our grand Foe,
Who now triumphs, and in the excess of joy
Sole reigning, holds the tyranny of Heaven.

JOHN MILTON
Satan from
"Paradise Lost"

CHILIASM

When I look into the mountain air
God looks into me;
That is my statement,
That is my authority.

But when I dive into the sea
And swim in choking wrath
By the throat Satan shakes me,
Shakes me. My life he has.

So when I stand on the sea shore
Looking into the mountains,
Looking into the sea,
God and Devil are in me.

I am Love and I am Wrath.

RICHARD EBERHART

DOVER BEACH

The sea is calm to-night,
The tide is full, the moon lies fair
Upon the Straits;—on the French coast the light
Gleams, and is gone; the cliffs of England stand,
Glimmering and vast, out in the tranquil bay.
Come to the window, sweet is the night-air!
Only, from the lone line of spray
Where the sea meets the moon-blanch'd land,
Listen! you hear the grating roar
Of pebbles which the waves draw back and fling,
At their return, up the high strand,
Begin, and cease, and then again begin,
With tremulous cadence slow, and bring
The eternal note of sadness in.

Sophocles long ago
Heard it on the Ægean, and it brought
Into his mind the turbid ebb and flow
Of human misery; we
Find also in the sound a thought,
Hearing it by this distant northern sea.

The Sea of Faith
Was once, too, at the full, and round earth's shore
Lay like the folds of a bright girdle furl'd.
But now I only hear
Its melancholy, long, withdrawing roar,
Retreating, to the breath
Of the night-wind, down the vast edges drear
And naked shingles of the world.

Ah, love, let us be true
To one another! for the world, which seems
To lie before us like a land of dreams,
So various, so beautiful, so new,
Hath really neither joy, nor love, nor light,
Nor certitude, nor peace, nor help for pain;
And we are here as on a darkling plain
Swept with confused alarms of struggle and flight,
Where ignorant armies clash by night.

MATTHEW ARNOLD

PRAISE DOUBT

Praise the good angel doubt,
Guardian of us that walk
On the deep waters of this world.

Praise him. He never rests,
However weary the way
Over these dark, salt, dangerous meadows.

Do not look down, he says;
Beware with me and the sun
Of faith's innumerable caverns.

Monsters can be there.
You will have plenty of time.
Too soon descending, you are devoured.

Praise him. He believes
In the long day we are given.
Praise him. He dances upon the whitecaps.

MARK VAN DOREN

OH YET WE TRUST
THAT SOMEHOW GOOD

Oh yet we trust that somehow good
  Will be the final goal of ill,
  To pangs of nature, sins of will,
Defects of doubt, and taints of blood;

That nothing walks with aimless feet;
  That not one life shall be destroy'd,
  Or cast as rubbish to the void,
When God hath made the pile complete;

That not a worm is cloven in vain;
  That not a moth with vain desire
  Is shrivell'd in a fruitless fire,
Or but subserves another's gain.

Behold, we know not anything;
  I can but trust that good shall fall
  At last—far off—at last, to all,
And every winter change to spring.

So runs my dream: but what am I?
  An infant crying in the night;
  An infant crying for the light:
And with no language but a cry.

ALFRED, LORD TENNYSON
From
"In Memoriam"

THE GREAT MAGICIANS

To fish for pearls in Lethe,
Wash gold from age-long grief;
To give infinity a frame,
The may-fly a reprieve:

In a calm phrase to utter
The wild and wandering sky;
To reconcile a lover's Eden
With a madman's sty:

To mediate between
The candle and the moth;
To plug time's dripping wound, or spin
A web across hell's mouth:

Such feats the great magicians
Found within their powers,
Whose quick illusions bodied out
A world more whole than ours.

But the hollow in the breast
Where a God should be—
This is the fault they may not
Absolve nor remedy.

C. DAY LEWIS

FALSE GODS

From gods of other men, fastidious heart,
You thank your stars good sense
               has set you free.
Ay. But the dread slow piercing of
               death's dart?
Its, 'Why, my God, have I forsaken thee?'

WALTER DE LA MARE

PRAYER

Let us not look upon
Their like again,
This generation
Of bewildered men—
With earth-roads, sea-roads,
Sky-roads, too, that show
All ways to enter
And no way to go.

WITTER BYNNER

DIDYMUS

Refusing to fall in love with God, he gave
Himself to the love of created things,
Accepting only what he could see, a river
Full of the shadows of swallows' wings

That dipped and skimmed the water; he would not
Ask where the water ran or why.
When he died, a swallow seemed to plunge
Into the reflected, the wrong, sky.

LOUIS MACNEICE

THE VILLAGE ATHEIST

Ye young debaters over the doctrine
Of the soul's immortality,
I who lie here was the village atheist,
Talkative, contentious, versed in the arguments
Of the infidels.
But through a long sickness
Coughing myself to death
I read the Upanishads and the poetry of Jesus.
And they lighted a torch of hope and intuition
And desire which the Shadow,
Leading me swiftly through the caverns of darkness,
Could not extinguish.
Listen to me, ye who live in the senses
And think through the senses only:
Immortality is not a gift,
Immortality is an achievement;
And only those who strive mightily
Shall possess it.

EDGAR LEE MASTERS

CRAG JACK'S APOSTASY

The churches, lord, all the dark churches
Stooped over my cradle once:
I came clear, but my god's down
Under the weight of all that stone:
Both my power and my luck since
Have kicked at the world and slept in ditches.

I do not desire to change my ways,
But now call continually
On you, god or not god, who
Come to my sleeping body through
The world under the world; pray
That I may see more than your eyes

In an animal's dreamed head; that I shall—
Waking, dragged suddenly
From a choir-shaken height
By the world, lord, and its dayfall—
Keep more than the memory
Of a wolf's head, of eagles' feet.

TED HUGHES

EASTER HYMN

If in that Syrian garden, ages slain,
You sleep, and know not you are dead in vain,
Nor even in dreams behold how dark and bright
Ascends in smoke and fire by day and night
The hate you died to quench and could but fan,
Sleep well and see no morning, son of man.

But if, the grave rent and the stone rolled by,
At the right hand of majesty on high
You sit, and sitting so remember yet
Your tears, your agony and bloody sweat,
Your cross and passion and the life you gave,
Bow hither out of heaven and see and save.

A. E. HOUSMAN

"THOU ART INDEED JUST, LORD, IF I CONTEND"

Justus quidem tu es, Domine, si disputem tecum:
verumtamen justa loquar ad te: Quare vio impiorum
prosperatur? etc.

JEREMIAH 12:1 *(Vulgate)*

Thou art indeed just, Lord, if I contend
With thee; but, sir, so what I plead is just.
Why do sinners' ways prosper? and why must
Disappointment all I endeavour end?
Wert thou my enemy, O thou my friend,
How wouldst thou worse, I wonder, than thou dost
Defeat, thwart me? Oh, the sots and thralls of lust
Do in spare hours more thrive than I that spend,
Sir, life upon thy cause. See, banks and brakes
Now, leavèd how thick! lacèd they are again
With fretty chervil, look, and fresh wind shakes
Them; birds build—but not I build; no, but strain,
Time's eunuch, and not breed one work that wakes.
Mine, O thou lord of life, send my roots rain.

GERARD MANLEY HOPKINS

A CHRISTMAS SONNET

FOR ONE IN DOUBT

While you that in your sorrow disavow
Service and hope, see love and brotherhood
Far off as ever, it will do no good
For you to wear his thorns upon your brow
For doubt of him. And should you question how
To serve him best, he might say, if he could,
"Whether or not the cross was made of wood
Whereon you nailed me, is no matter now."

Though other saviors have in older lore
A Legend, and for older gods have died—
Though death may wear the crown it always wore
And ignorance be still the sword of pride—
Something is here that was not here before,
And strangely has not yet been crucified.

EDWIN ARLINGTON ROBINSON

THE TRIUMPH OF DOUBT

There is so much loveliness gone out of the world:
  There is left but the violet dusk of the wood
    And the slow wavering of grey-blue hills on the sky.
The dead grass is silent and the dead leafage whirled
  Down the long lanes of silent air. The barberry
Drips from its twisted crown of thorns slow drops of blood.

These are the days when the soul is less than a leaf
  Blown through the shrivelled grass or left on the frozen sod;
    For these, if they fail, fail with one more sure than they.
Now doubt stands long by the murdered bed of relief
  And feels for his own side; the soul stares at decay,
  That turns slowly, triumphantly, swiftly to God.

JOHN PEALE BISHOP

THOUGH THE GREAT WATERS SLEEP

Though the great Waters sleep,
That they are still the Deep,
We cannot doubt—
No vacillating God
Ignited this Abode
To put it out—

EMILY DICKINSON

THE NATURE OF LOVE

The sun, God's eye,
Is infinite, its rays
Ungraspable, except
By a sharpened gaze.

Its love is all.
Yet we must give our sight
To convert a fraction
Of its open light.

Only the heart that makes
A prism of its doubt
Can split the infinite of light
That shutters nothing out.

JAMES KIRKUP

THE COLLAR

I struck the board, and cry'd, No more.
        I will abroad.
    What? shall I ever sigh and pine?
My lines and life are free; free as the road,
    Loose as the winde, as large as store.
        Shall I be still in suit?
Have I no harvest but a thorn
To let me blood, and not restore
What I have lost with cordiall fruit?
        Sure there was wine
Before my sighs did drie it: there was corn
    Before my tears did drown it.
    Is the yeare onely lost to me?
        Have I no bayes to crown it?
No flowers, no garlands gay? all blasted?
        All wasted?
Not so my heart: but there is fruit,
    And thou hast hands.
Recover all thy sigh-blown age
On double pleasures: leave thy cold dispute
Of what is fit, and not. Forsake thy cage,
        Thy rope of sands,
Which pettie thoughts have made, and made to thee
    Good cable, to enforce and draw,
        And be thy law,
While thou didst wink and wouldst not see.
        Away; take heed:
        I will abroad.
Call in thy deaths head there: tie up thy fears.
        He that forbears
    To suit and serve his need,
        Deserves his load.

But as I rav'd and grew more fierce and wilde
At every worde,
Methought I heard one calling, *Childe!*
And I reply'd, *My Lord.*

GEORGE HERBERT

GOD'S
FAMILIARS

WHEN THE SAINTS GO MARCHIN' IN

O when the saints go marchin' in,
O when the saints go marchin' in,
Lord, I want to be in that number
When the saints go marchin' in.

O when the day of judgment comes,
O when the day of judgment comes,
Lord, I want to be in that number
When the saints go marchin' in.

NEGRO SPIRITUAL

BEAUTEOUS, YEA BEAUTEOUS
MORE THAN THESE

Beauteous, yea beauteous more than these,
The Shepherd King upon his knees,
    For his momentous trust;
With wish of infinite conceit,
For man, beast, mute, the small and great,
    And prostrate dust to dust.

CHRISTOPHER SMART
From
"A Song to David"

THE PROPHET

Athirst in spirit, through the gloom
Of an unpeopled waste I blundered,
And saw a six-winged Seraph loom
Where the two pathways met and sundered.
He set his fingers on my eyes:
His touch lay soft as slumber lies—
And like an eagle's, scared and shaken,
Did my prophetic eyes awaken.
He touched my ears, and lo! they rang
With a reverberating clang:
I heard the spheres revolving, chiming,
The angels in their soaring sweep,
The monsters moving in the deep,
The vines low in the valley climbing.
And from my mouth the Seraph wrung
Forth by its roots my sinful tongue,
The idle tongue that slyly babbled,
The vain, malicious, the unchaste,
And the wise serpent's sting he placed
In my numb mouth with hand blood-dabbled;
And with a sword he clove my breast,
Drew forth the heart that shook with dread
And in my gaping bosom pressed
A glowing coal of fire instead.

Upon the wastes, a lifeless clod,
I lay, and heard the voice of God:
"Arise, O prophet, look and ponder:
Arise, charged with my will and spurred!
As over roads and seas you wander,
Kindle men's hearts with this, my Word."

ALEXANDER PUSHKIN
Translated by
Babette Deutsch

THREE HELPERS IN BATTLE

I have not been as Joshua when he fought
The hosts of Amalek in the valley found.
My voice hath never, like a trumpet sound,
Victory for the falling victors wrought.
But I, with Aaron, faint yet unafraid,
Held up the hands of Moses while he prayed.

MARY COLERIDGE

THE ANGELS CAME A-MUSTERING

The Angels came a-mustering,
    A-mustering, a-mustering,
The Angels came a-clustering
    Around the sapphire throne.

A-questioning of one another,
    Of one another, of one another,
A-questioning each one his brother
    Around the sapphire throne.

Pray who is he, and where is he,
    And where is he, and where is he,
Whose shining cast—so fair is he—
    A shadow on the throne?

Pray, who has up to heaven come,
    To heaven come, to heaven come,
Through all the circles seven come,
    To fetch the Torah down?

'Tis Moses up to heaven come,
    To heaven come, to heaven come,
Through all the circles seven come,
    To fetch the Torah down!

ANONYMOUS
Translated by
Israel Zangwill

GO DOWN, MOSES

When Israel was in Egypt's land,
    Let my people go!
Oppressed so hard they could not stand,
    Let my people go!

    Go down, Moses,
    'Way down in Egypt's land,
    Tell old Pharaoh
    To let my people go!

"Thus spake the Lord," bold Moses said,
    "Let my people go!
If not, I'll smite your firstborn dead,
    Let my people go!"

    Go down, Moses,
    'Way down in Egypt's land,
    Tell old Pharaoh
    To let my people go!

"No more shall they in bondage toil,
    Let my people go!
Let them come out with Egypt's spoil,
    Let my people go!"

    Go down, Moses,
    'Way down in Egypt's land,
    Tell old Pharaoh
    To let my people go!

NEGRO SPIRITUAL

THE MURDER OF MOSES

By reason of despair we set forth behind you
And followed the pillar of fire like a doubt,
To hold to belief wanted a sign,
Called the miracle of the staff and the plagues
Natural phenomena.

We questioned the expediency of the march,
Gossiped about you. What was escape
To the fear of going forward and Pharaoh's wheels?
When the chariots mired and the army flooded
Our cry of horror was one with theirs.

You always went alone, a little ahead,
Prophecy disturbed you, you were not a fanatic.
The women said you were meek, the men
Regarded you as a typical leader.
You and your black wife might have been foreigners.

We even discussed your parentage; were you really a Jew?
We remembered how Joseph had made himself a prince,
All of us shared in the recognition, sense of propriety,
Devotion to his brothers and Israel.

We hated you daily. Our children died. The water spilled.
It was as if you were trying to lose us one by one.
Our wandering seemed the wandering of your mind,
The cloud believed we were tireless,
We expressed our contempt and our boredom openly.

At last you ascended the rock; at last returned.
Your anger that day was probably His.
When we saw you come down from the mountain, your
                                          skin alight

And the stones of our law flashing,
We fled like animals and the dancers scattered.

We watched where you overturned the calf on the fire,
We hid when you broke the tablets on the rock,
We wept when we drank the mixture of gold and water.
We had hoped you were lost or had left us.
This was the day of our greatest defilement.

You were simple of heart; you were sorry for Miriam,
You reasoned with Aaron, who was your enemy.
However often you cheered us with songs and prayers
We cursed you again. The serpents bit us,
And mouth to mouth you entreated the Lord for our sake.

At the end of it all we gave you the gift of death.
Invasion and generalship were spared you.
The hand of our direction, resignedly you fell,
And while officers prepared for the river crossing
The One God blessed you and covered you with earth.

Though you were mortal and once committed murder
You assumed the burden of the covenant,
Spoke for the world and for our understanding.
Converse with God made you a thinker,
Taught us all early justice, made us a race.

KARL SHAPIRO

103

JOB

They did not know this face
Where the chin rested on the sunken breastbone,
So changed it was, emptied, rinsed out and dried,
And for some future purpose put aside.
Expecting torment, they were much perplexed.

His world had gone
And he sat isolated, foul and flyblown,
Without a world, with nothing but a mind
Staggered to silence since it could not find
Language to utter its amazing text.

For where was Job?
In some strange state, unknown and yet well-known,
A mask that stared hollowly in God's breath,
Mind that perceived the irrelevance of death,
And the astonished heart unmoved, unvexed.

They did not see his soul
Perched like a bird upon the broken hearthstone,
Piping incessantly above the ashes
What next what next what next what next what next

ELIZABETH SEWELL

IN THE WILDERNESS

He, of his gentleness,
Thirsting and hungering
Walked in the wilderness;
Soft words of grace he spoke
Unto lost desert-folk
That listened wondering.
He heard the bittern call
From ruined palace-wall,
Answered him brotherly;
He held communion
With the she-pelican
Of lonely piety.
Basilisk, cockatrice,
Flocked to his homilies,
With mail of dread device,
With monstrous barbèd stings,
With eager dragon-eyes;
Great bats on leathern wings
And old, blind, broken things
Mean in their miseries.
Then ever with him went,
Of all his wanderings
Comrade, with ragged coat,
Gaunt ribs—poor innocent—
Bleeding foot, burning throat,
The guileless young scapegoat:
For forty nights and days
Followed in Jesus' ways,
Sure guard behind him kept.
Tears like a lover wept.

ROBERT GRAVES

105

SAINT JOHN THE BAPTIST

The last and greatest Herald of Heaven's King,
Girt with rough skins, hies to the deserts wild,
Among that savage brood the woods forth bring,
Which he than man more harmless found and mild.
His food was locusts, and what young doth spring,
With honey that from virgin hives distill'd;
Parch'd body, hollow eyes, some uncouth thing
Made him appear, long since from earth exiled.
There burst he forth: 'All ye, whose hopes rely
On God, with me amidst these deserts mourn;
Repent, repent, and from old errors turn!'
Who listen'd to his voice, obey'd his cry?
Only the echoes, which he made relent,
Rung from their marble caves 'Repent! Repent!'

WILLIAM DRUMMOND

A REVIVALIST IN BOSTON

But you shall walk the golden street
And you unhouse and house the Lord.

Going home by lamplight across Boston Common,
We heard him tell how God had entered in him,
And now he had the Word, and nothing other
Would do but he must cry it to his brother.

We stood and listened there—to nothing new.
Yet something loosed his tongue and drove him
                                        shouting.
Compulsion's not play-acted in a face,
And he was telling us the way to grace.

Somehow we saw the youth that he had been,
Not one to notice; an ordinary boy—
Hardly the one the Lord would make His tool—
Shuffling his feet in Baptist Sunday school.

And then transfiguration came his way;
He knew the secret all the rest were seeking.
He made the tale of Christendom his own,
And hoarsely called his brethren to the throne.

The same old way; and yet we knew he saw
The angelic hosts whose names he stumbled over.
He made us hear the ranks of shining feet
Treading to glory's throne up Tremont Street.

ADRIENNE CECILE RICH

CONVERSATION IN AVILA

Teresa was God's familiar. She often spoke
To Him informally,
As if together they shared some heavenly joke.
Once, watching stormily
Her heart's ambitions wither to odds and ends,
With all to start anew,
She cried, "If this is the way You treat Your friends,
No wonder You have so few!"

There is no perfect record standing by
Of God's reply.

PHYLLIS MC GINLEY

THE THUNDERER

God's angry man, His crotchety scholar,
Was Saint Jerome,
The great name-caller,
Who cared not a dime
For the laws of libel
And in his spare time
Translated the Bible.
Quick to disparage
All joys but learning,
Jerome thought marriage
Better than burning;
But didn't like woman's
Painted cheeks;
Didn't like Romans,
Didn't like Greeks,
Hated Pagans
For their Pagan ways,
Yet doted on Cicero all his days.

A born reformer, cross and gifted,
He scolded mankind
Sterner than Swift did;
Worked to save
The world from the heathen;
Fled to a cave
For peace to breathe in,
Promptly wherewith
For miles around
He filled the air with
Fury and sound.
In a mighty prose
For almighty ends,
He thrust at his foes,
Quarreled with his friends,

And served his Master,
Though with complaint.
He wasn't a plaster
Sort of saint.

But he swelled men's minds
With a Christian leaven.
It takes all kinds
To make a Heaven.

PHYLLIS MC GINLEY

SAINT FRANCIS

The curé in his windy gown
Wildly stops and lifts his sleeves
To bless the flight that flutters down,
Late yellow flock of beechen leaves.

Bewildered by their wings he stands
And overcomes the wind with words,
An old daft man with helpless hands,
Saint Francis preaching to the birds.

JOHN PEALE BISHOP

A FOREIGNER COMES TO EARTH
ON BOSTON COMMON

In the shadow of Old South Church the turn of spring is
Slow, melancholy rain from eaves and branches:
There is the smell of clay that once had been
Eyes that feared heaven, hair delicate to touch,
Lips that almost parted to drink, to weep, to smile.

                      It is reported
One can hear voices running through the grasses,
And at evening whinnying between brick walls.
There, as rain falls, the text is found:
"Vanity," saith the Preacher, "is a rainbow
Glittering against clouds that are filled with tears,
Fold within fold,
Coral in amber, emerald in amethyst,
And is the arc of that crystal ball which is the world."

                     Sunset discovered
A figure standing between trees and traffic
Unmindful of the dark behind the Common,
Or of approaching night, or of draughts and storms;
He stood as though he felt
The noon of summer in his heart and the sun streaming
Within the veins of his thin arms.

                    One could almost hear
His fingers call the birds,
Striking and straying, as if they tuned a violin,
Invisible strings of music in the air:
"Sister Water, Brother Fire,
Earth and her Seasons whose lips are roses,
Whose breasts are lilies;
Welcome all the creatures in flowery dress,

And in thy circle bring pale Bodily Death
Who walks like a woman weeping behind her veils
And gathers the living with her under grass."

      Then to him came
A multitude of wrens, the jade-green parakeet,
Wild dove, hawk-sparrow, the flickering
Virginian nightingale, the mothlike Dusty Miller
Flying and fluttering to his knees and shoulders.
When the wings stilled, he began to tell them
Of trees that grew barren at the top,
Of towers that suddenly filled with light, then
        fell to ashes,
Of the capricious laws of birds and men,
Of the circular blue and golden joys of heaven.

     After the birds had flown,
Those who saw him spoke of his archaic head,
Thin nostrils, dark face and transparent body
That rose in air through which night gleamed and stirred.

      One had heard him say:
"To see the world without profit or grief
One must lean into it as through an open window;
Waterfalls and rocks abound there,
Flowers and vines, meadows of wheat,
White alps and purple valleys—
After that vision, the gray Serpent who drinks the ocean
And eats the heart and mind
Is nothing but a dream."

      It was agreed
That what he saw could not resemble Boston:
He had talked of meeting angels in the street,
Of a flaming bush that could not have grown
In Copley Square. Some said it was fortunate
That he did not return; others that birds had not
        been known

To sing praises of men. It was clear that no one
                              but a saint
Could speak as he did and not have his eyes
Plucked out by nervous crows.

HORACE GREGORY

THE BALLAD OF FATHER GILLIGAN

The old priest Peter Gilligan
Was weary night and day;
For half his flock were in their beds,
Or under green sods lay.

Once, while he nodded on a chair,
At the moth-hour of eve,
Another poor man sent for him,
And he began to grieve.

'I have no rest, nor joy, nor peace,
For people die and die';
And after cried he, 'God forgive!
My body spake, not I!'
He knelt, and leaning on the chair
He prayed and fell asleep;
And the moth-hour went from the fields,
And stars began to peep.

They slowly into millions grew,
And leaves shook in the wind;
And God covered the world with shade,
And whispered to mankind.

Upon the time of sparrow-chirp
When the moths came once more,
The old priest Peter Gilligan
Stood upright on the floor.

'Mavrone, mavrone! the man has died
While I slept on the chair';
He roused his horse out of its sleep,
And rode with little care.

He rode now as he never rode,
By rocky lane and fen;
The sick man's wife opened the door:
'Father! you come again!'

'And is the poor man dead?' he cried.
'He died an hour ago.'
The old priest Peter Gilligan
In grief swayed to and fro.

'When you were gone, he turned and died
As merry as a bird.'
The old priest Peter Gilligan
He knelt him at the word.

'He Who hath made the night of stars
For souls who tire and bleed,
Sent one of His great angels down
To help me in my need.

'He Who is wrapped in purple robes,
With planets in His care,
Had pity on the least of things
Asleep upon a chair.'

WILLIAM BUTLER YEATS

SANTOS: NEW MEXICO

Return to the most human, nothing less
Will nourish the torn spirit, the bewildered heart,
The angry mind: and from the ultimate duress,
Pierced with the breath of anguish, speak for love.

Return, return to the deep sources, nothing less
Will teach the stiff hands a new way to serve,
To carve into our lives the forms of tenderness
And still that ancient necessary pain preserve.

O we have moved too far from these, all we who look
Upon the wooden painted figure, stiff and quaint,
Reading it curiously like a legend in a book—
But it is Man upon the cross. It is the living saint.

To those who breathed their faith into the wood
It was no image, but the very living source,
The saviour of their own humanity by blood
That flows terribly like a river in its course.

They did not fear the strangeness, nor while gazing
Keep from this death their very precious life.
They looked until their hands and hearts were blazing
And the reality of pain pierced like a knife.

We must go down into the dungeons of the heart,
To the dark places where modern mind imprisons
All that is not defined and though apart.
We must let out the terrible creative visions.

Return to the most human, nothing less
Will teach the angry spirit, the bewildered heart,
The torn mind, to accept the whole of its duress,
And pierced with anguish, at last act for love.

MAY SARTON

116

SAINTS

Not all of them must suffer. Some,
once spoken for, once chosen, sing
of flawless weather in a jewelled city
turning and burning in the sun.

St. Anthony saw nightmares, and a wheel
still gives a name to Catherine's agony.
St. Sebastian took his feathered glory
as a magnet draws slim files of steel.

Others we honor lived a while
in landscapes crueler than the moon.
They learned by heart the sirens' tune.
They knew the tiger's brightest smile.

The rest are called, not chosen, must
daily put on old armor and ride out
to meet the dragon. They love the songs
of joyous saints whose tongues are holy dust.

GEORGE GARRETT

117

ALL
CREATURES
HERE
BELOW

SAY NOT THE STRUGGLE
NAUGHT AVAILETH

Say not the struggle naught availeth,
　　The labour and the wounds are vain,
The enemy faints not, nor faileth,
　　And as things have been they remain.

If hopes were dupes, fears may be liars;
　　It may be, in yon smoke conceal'd,
Your comrades chase e'en now the fliers,
　　And, but for you, possess the field.

For while the tired waves, vainly breaking,
　　Seem here no painful inch to gain,
Far back through creeks and inlets making,
　　Comes silent, flooding in, the main.

And not by eastern windows only,
　　When daylight comes, comes in the light;
In front the sun climbs slow, how slowly!
　　But westward, look, the land is bright!

ARTHUR HUGH CLOUGH

ETERNITY'S LOW VOICE

Eternity's low voice,
That no one yet has heard,
Sings peace be with you, children
Of man, beast, worm, and bird.

MARK VAN DOREN

THE BOOK OF KELLS

Out of the living word
Come flower, serpent and bird.

All things that swim or fly
Or go upon the ground,
All shapes that breath can cry
Into the sinews of sound,
That growth can make abound
In the river of the eye
Till speech is three-ply
And the truth triply wound.

Out of the living word
Come flower, serpent and bird.

HOWARD NEMEROV

PIED BEAUTY

Glory be to God for dappled things—
   For skies of couple-colour as a brinded cow;
     For rose-moles all in stipple upon trout that swim;
Fresh-firecoal chestnut-falls, finches' wings;
   Landscape plotted and pieced—fold, fallow, and plough;
     And all trades, their gear and tackle and trim.

All things counter, original, spare, strange;
   Whatever is fickle, freckled (who knows how?)
     With swift, slow; sweet, sour, adazzle, dim;
He fathers-forth whose beauty is past change:
                 Praise him.

GERARD MANLEY HOPKINS

FRANCIS JAMMES: A PRAYER TO GO TO PARADISE WITH THE DONKEYS

TO MAÍRE AND JACK

When I must come to you, O my God, I pray
It be some dusty-roaded holiday,
And even as my travels here below,
I beg to choose by what road I shall go
To Paradise, where the clear stars shine by day.
I'll take my walking-stick and go my way,
And to my friends the donkeys I shall say,
"I am Francis Jammes, and I'm going to Paradise,
For there is no hell in the land of the loving God."

And I'll say to them: "Come, sweet friends of the blue skies,
Poor creatures who with a flap of the ears or a nod
Of the head shake off the buffets, the bees, the flies . . . "

Let me come with these donkeys, Lord, into your land,
These beasts who bow their heads so gently, and stand
With their small feet joined together in a fashion
Utterly gentle, asking your compassion.
I shall arrive, followed by their thousands of ears,
Followed by those with baskets at their flanks,
By those who lug the carts of mountebanks
Or loads of feather-dusters and kitchen-wares,
By those with humps of battered water-cans,
By bottle-shaped she-asses who halt and stumble,
By those tricked out in little pantaloons
To cover their wet, blue galls where flies assemble
In whirling swarms, making a drunken hum.

Dear God, let it be with these donkeys that I come,
And let it be that angels lead us in peace
To leafy streams where cherries tremble in air,
Sleek as the laughing flesh of girls; and there
In that haven of souls let it be that, leaning above
Your divine waters, I shall resemble these donkeys,
Whose humble and sweet poverty will appear
Clear in the clearness of your eternal love.

RICHARD WILBUR

DONKEY

Whose little beast?
Somebody owned him.
Some great angel,
I think, loaned him,
Smiling, to men;
And wants him again.

How can he leave us?
Where will he go?
He is half in love
With living below,
And habit is strong.
He has been here long.

Stoic for nothing.
Yet he will start.
Heaven must have him,
Stubborn of heart
And stiffened of hair
Even then, even there.

MARK VAN DOREN

CAT AND MOUSE

On the sheep-cropped summit, under hot sun,
The mouse crouched, staring out the chance
It dared not take.
       Time and a world
Too old to alter, the five mile prospect—
Woods, villages, farms—hummed its heat-heavy
Stupor of life.
       Whether to two
Feet or four, how are prayers contracted!
Whether in God's eye or the eye of a cat.

TED HUGHES

THE BLINDED BIRD

So zestfully canst thou sing?
And all this indignity,
With God's consent, on thee!
Blinded ere yet a-wing
By the red-hot needle thou,
I stand and wonder how
So zestfully thou canst sing!

Resenting not such wrong,
Thy grievous pain forgot,
Eternal dark thy lot,
Groping thy whole life long,
After that stab of fire;
Enjailed in pitiless wire;
Resenting not such wrong!

Who hath charity? This bird.
Who suffereth long and is kind,
Is not provoked, though blind
And alive ensepulchred?
Who hopeth, endureth all things?
Who thinketh no evil, but sings?
Who is divine? This bird.

THOMAS HARDY

THE WINDHOVER:

TO CHRIST OUR LORD

I caught this morning's minion, king-
   dom of daylight's dauphin, dapple-dawn-drawn Falcon, in
                         his riding
   Of the rolled level underneath him steady air, and striding
High there, how he rung upon the rein of a wimpling wing
In his ecstasy! then off, off forth on swing,
   As a skate's heel sweeps smooth on a bow-bend: the hurl
                         and gliding
   Rebuffed the big wind. My heart in hiding
Stirred for a bird,—the achieve of, the mastery of the thing!

Brute beauty and valour and act, oh, air, pride, plume, here
   Buckle! AND the fire breaks from thee then, a billion
times told lovelier, more dangerous, O my chevalier!

   No wonder of it: shéer plód makes plough down sillion
Shine, and blue-bleak embers, ah my dear,
   Fall, gall themselves, and gash gold-vermilion.

GERARD MANLEY HOPKINS

LITTLE THINGS

Little things, that run, and quail,
And die, in silence and despair!

Little things, that fight, and fail,
And fall, on sea, and earth, and air!

All trapped and frightened little things,
The mouse, the coney, hear our prayer!

As we forgive those done to us,
—The lamb, the linnet, and the hare—

Forgive us all our trespasses,
Little creatures, everywhere!

JAMES STEPHENS

THE BELLS OF HEAVEN

'Twould ring the bells of Heaven
The wildest peal for years,
If Parson lost his senses
And people came to theirs,
And he and they together
Knelt down with angry prayers
For tamed and shabby tigers
And dancing dogs and bears,
And wretched, blind pit ponies,
And little hunted hares.

RALPH HODGSON

UP FROM THE BED OF THE RIVER

Up from the bed of the river
God scooped the clay;
And by the bank of the river
He kneeled him down;
And there the great God Almighty
Who lit the sun and fixed it in the sky
Who flung the stars to the most far corner of the night,
Who rounded the earth in the middle of his hand;
This Great God,
Like a mammy bending over her baby,
Kneeled down in the dust
Toiling over a lump of clay
Till he shaped it in his own image;

Then into it he blew the breath of life,
And man became a living soul.
Amen.   Amen.

JAMES WELDON JOHNSON
From
"The Creation"

MAN IS GOD'S NATURE

The god would come, the god would go.
    The wind is never seen, but it is known
    In pelt of rain, in lace of snow.
So through our sense is godhead blown.

The least elusive master imprint
    Taken in the impression of our faces
    Is a look not spirit's hint,
And more than intellectual graces.

The character that makes the form
    Is spiritual fact, that stands upon the flesh
    Becoming at least the human norm:
There the god is ever fresh.

We do not see the god, but give it
    In the subtlety of happy lineaments,
    When all our passions have been lit;
Godhead in the mortal element.

RICHARD EBERHART

AS KINGFISHERS CATCH FIRE

As kingfishers catch fire, dragonflies dráw fláme;
As tumbled over rim in roundy wells
Stones ring; like each tucked string tells,
            each hung bell's
Bow swung finds tongue to fling out broad its name;
Each mortal thing does one thing and the same;
Deals out that being indoors each one dwells;
Selves—goes itself; *myself* it speaks and spells;
Crying *Whát I dó is me: for that I came.*

Í say móre: the just man justices;
Kéeps gráce: thát keeps all his goings graces;
Acts in God's eye what in God's eye he is—
Chríst—for Christ plays in ten thousand places,
Lovely in limbs, and lovely in eyes not his
To the Father through the features of men's faces.

GERARD MANLEY HOPKINS

SON AND FATHER

By the glim of a midwinterish early morning
Following habit's track over comatose fields,
A path of bleak reminder, I go to receive
The sacraments from my father, thirty years back.

Afterwards, walking home, unannealed, implacable,
I knew in the bones of my age this numb, flayed air,
These frozen grassblades rasping the foot, those hoar-drops
Which hung from a branch all day like unredeemed pledges.

Oh, black frost of my youth, recalcitrant time
When love's seed was benighted and gave no ear
To other's need, you were seasonable, you were
In nature: but were you as well my nature's blight?

That was thirty years back. The father is dead whose image
And superscription upon me I had to efface
Or myself be erased. Did I thus, denying him, grow
Quite dead to the Father's grace, the Son's redemption?

Ungenerous to him no more, but unregenerate,
Still on a frozen earth I stumble after
Each glimmer of God, although it lights up my lack,
And lift my maimed creations to beg rebirth.

C. DAY LEWIS

STRONG SON OF GOD

Strong Son of God, immortal Love,
    Whom we, that have not seen thy face,
    By faith, and faith alone, embrace,
Believing where we cannot prove;

Thine are these orbs of light and shade;
    Thou madest Life in man and brute;
    Thou madest Death; and lo, thy foot
Is on the skull which thou hast made.

Thou wilt not leave us in the dust:
    Thou madest man, he knows not why,
    He thinks he was not made to die;
And thou hast made him: thou art just.

Thou seemest human and divine,
    The highest, holiest manhood, thou:
    Our wills are ours, we know not how;
Our wills are ours, to make them thine.

Our little systems have their day;
    They have their day and cease to be:
    They are but broken lights of thee,
And thou, O Lord, art more than they.

We have but faith: we cannot know,
    For knowledge is of things we see;
    And yet we trust it comes from thee,
A beam in darkness: let it grow.

Let knowledge grow from more to more,
    But more of reverence in us dwell;
    That mind and soul, according well,
May make one music as before,

But vaster. We are fools and slight;
    We mock thee when we do not fear:
    But help thy foolish ones to bear;
Help thy vain worlds to bear thy light.

Forgive what seem'd my sin in me,
    What seem'd my worth since I began;
    For merit lives from man to man,
And not from man, O Lord, to thee.

Forgive my grief for one removed,
    Thy creature, whom I found so fair.
    I trust he lives in thee, and there
I find him worthier to be loved.

Forgive these wild and wandering cries,
    Confusions of a wasted youth;
    Forgive them where they fail in truth,
And in thy wisdom, make me wise.

ALFRED, LORD TENNYSON
From
"In Memoriam"

WHAT ARE YEARS?

What is our innocence,
what is our guilt? All are
    naked, none is safe. And whence
is courage: the unanswered question,
the resolute doubt,—
dumbly calling, deafly listening—that
in misfortune, even death,
    encourages others
    and in its defeat, stirs

the soul to be strong? He
sees deep and is glad, who
    accedes to mortality
and in his imprisonment rises
upon himself as
the sea in a chasm, struggling to be
free and unable to be,
    in its surrendering
    finds its continuing.

So he who strongly feels,
behaves. The very bird,
    grown taller as he sings, steels
his form straight up. Though he is captive,
his mighty singing
says, satisfaction is a lowly
thing, how pure a thing is joy.
    This is mortality.
    This is eternity.

MARIANNE MOORE

A LYKE-WAKE DIRGE

This ae nighte, this ae nighte,
   —Every nighte and alle,
Fire and fleet and candle-lighte,
   And Christe receive thy saule.

When thou from hence away art past,
   —Every nighte and alle,
To Whinny-muir thou com'st at last;
   And Christe receive thy saule.

If ever thou gavest hosen and shoon,
   —Every nighte and alle,
Sit thee down and put them on;
   And Christe receive thy saule.

If hosen and shoon thou ne'er gav'st nane
   —Every nighte and alle,
The whinnes sall prick thee to the bare bane;
   And Christe receive thy saule.

From Whinny-muir when thou may'st pass,
   —Every nighte and alle,
To Brig o'Dread thou com'st at last;
   And Christe receive thy saule.

From Brig o'Dread when thou may'st pass.
   —Every nighte and alle,
To Purgatory fire thou com'st at last;
   And Christe receive thy saule.

If ever thou gavest meat or drink,
   —Every nighte and alle,
The fire sall never make thee shrink;
   And Christe receive thy saule.

If meat or drink thou ne'er gav'st nane,
  —*Every nighte and alle,*
The fire will burn thee to the bare bane;
  And Christe receive thy saule.

This ae nighte, this ae nighte,
  —*Every nighte and alle,*
Fire and fleet and candle-lighte,
  And Christe receive thy saule.

ANONYMOUS

*(Sixteenth century, found
by John Aubrey)*

THE SPARROW'S SKULL

MEMENTO MORI

(Written at the Fall of France)

The kingdoms fall in sequence, like the waves on the shore.
All save divine and desperate hopes go down, they are
$\qquad\qquad$ no more.
Solitary is our place, the castle in the sea,
And I muse on those I have loved, and on those who have
$\qquad\qquad$ loved me.

I gather up my loves, and keep them all warm,
While above our heads blows the bitter storm:
The blessed natural loves, of life-supporting flame,
And those whose name is Wonder, which have no other
$\qquad\qquad$ name.

The skull is in my hand, the minute cup of bone,
And I remember her, the tame, the loving one,
Who came in at the window, and seemed to have a mind
More towards sorrowful man than to those of her own kind.

She came for a long time, but at length she grew old;
And on her death-day she came, so feeble and so bold;
And all day, as if knowing what the day would bring,
She waited by the window, with her head beneath her wing.

And I will keep the skull, for in the hollow here
Lodged the minute brain that had outgrown a fear:
Transcended an old terror, and found a new love,
And entered a strange life, a world it was not of.

Even so, dread God! even so, my Lord!
The fire is at my feet, and at my breast the sword,
And I must gather up my soul, and clap my wings, and flee
Into the heart of terror, to find myself in thee.

$\qquad\qquad\qquad\qquad$ **RUTH PITTER**

141

THE MAN WITH THE HOE

God made man in His own image,
in the image of God he made him.

GENESIS

Bowed by the weight of centuries he leans
Upon his hoe and gazes on the ground,
The emptiness of ages in his face,
And on his back the burden of the world.
Who made him dead to rapture and despair,
A thing that grieves not and that never hopes,
Stolid and stunned, a brother to the ox?
Who loosened and let down this brutal jaw?
Whose was the hand that slanted back this brow?
Whose breath blew out the light within this brain?

Is this the Thing the Lord God made and gave
To have dominion over sea and land?
To trace the stars and search the heavens for power;
To feel the passion of Eternity?
Is this the dream He dreamed who shaped the suns
And marked their ways upon the ancient deep?
Down all the caverns of Hell to their last gulf
There is no shape more terrible than this—
More tongued with censure of the world's blind greed—
More filled with signs and portents for the soul—
More packt with danger to the universe.

What gulfs between him and the seraphim!
Slave of the wheel of labor, what to him
Are Plato and the swing of Pleiades?
What the long reaches of the peaks of song,
The rift of dawn, the reddening of the rose?
Through this dread shape the suffering ages look;

Time's tragedy is in that aching stoop;
Through this dread shape humanity betrayed,
Plundered, profaned and disinherited,
Cries protest to the Powers that made the world,
A protest that is also prophecy.

O masters, lords and rulers in all lands,
Is this the handiwork you give to God,
This monstrous thing distorted and soul-quencht?
How will you ever straighten up this shape;
Touch it again with immortality;
Give back the upward looking and the light;
Rebuild in it the music and the dream;
Make right the immemorial infamies,
Perfidious wrongs, immedicable woes?

O masters, lords and rulers in all lands,
How will the future reckon with this Man?
How answer his brute question in that hour
When whirlwinds of rebellion shake all shores?
How will it be with kingdoms and with kings—
With those who shaped him to the thing he is—
When this dumb Terror shall rise to judge the world,
After the silence of the centuries?

EDWIN MARKHAM

DIRGE FOR THE NEW SUNRISE

(Fifteen minutes past eight o'clock, on the morning of
Monday the 6th of August, 1945)

Bound to my heart as Ixion to the wheel,
Nailed to my heart as the Thief upon the Cross,
I hang between our Christ and the gap where the world
                                              was lost

And watch the phantom Sun in Famine Street—
The ghost of the heart of man . . . red Cain
And the more murderous brain
Of Man, still redder Nero that conceived the death
Of his mother Earth, and tore
Her womb, to know the place where he was conceived.

But no eyes grieved—
For none were left for tears:
They were blinded as the years
Since Christ was born. Mother or Murderer, you have
                          given or taken life—
Now all is one!

There was a morning when the holy Light
Was young . . . The beautiful First Creature came
To our water-springs, and thought us without blame.

Our hearts seemed safe in our breasts and sang to the Light—
The marrow in the bone
We dreamed was safe . . . the blood in the veins, the
                                     sap in the tree
Were springs of Deity.

But I saw the little-Ant men as they ran
Carrying the world's weight of the world's filth
And the filth in the heart of Man—
Compressed till those lusts and greeds had a greater heat
                              than that of the Sun.

And the ray from that heat came soundless, shook the sky
As if in search for food, and squeezed the stems
Of all that grows on the earth till they were dry—
And drank the marrow of the bone:
The eyes that saw, the lips that kissed, are gone—
Or black as thunder lie and grin at the murdered Sun.

The living blind and seeing Dead together lie
As if in love . . . There was no more hating then,
And no more love: Gone is the heart of Man.

EDITH SITWELL

IN DISTRUST OF MERITS

Strengthened to live, strengthened to die for
    medals and positioned victories?
They're fighting, fighting, fighting the blind
    man who thinks he sees,—
who cannot see that the enslaver is
enslaved; the hater, harmed, O shining O
        firm star, O tumultous
           ocean lashed till small things go
      as they will, the mountainous
        wave makes us who look, know

depth. Lost at sea before they fought! O
      star of David, star of Bethlehem,
O black imperial lion
    of the Lord—emblem
of a risen world—be joined at last, be
joined. There is hate's crown beneath which all is
        death; there's love's without which none
        is king; the blessed deeds bless
      the halo. As contagion
        of sickness makes sickness,

contagion of trust can make trust. They're
      fighting in deserts and caves, one by
one, in battalions and squadrons;
    they're fighting that I
may yet recover from the disease, My
Self; some have it lightly; some will die. 'Man
        wolf to man' and we devour
          ourselves. The enemy could not
      have made a greater breach in our
        defences. One pilot-
ing a blind man can escape him, but

Job disheartened by false comfort knew
that nothing can be so defeating
    as a blind man who
can see. O alive who are dead, who are
proud not to see, O small dust of the earth
       that walks so arrogantly,
          trust begets power and faith is
       an affectionate thing. We
        vow, we make this promise

to the fighting—it's a promise—'We'll
     never hate black, white, red, yellow, Jew,
Gentile, Untouchable.' We are
    not competent to
make our vows. With set jaw they are fighting,
fighting, fighting,—some we love whom we know,
      some we love but know not—that
        hearts may feel and not be numb.
      It cures me; or am I what
       I can't believe in? Some

in snow, some on crags, some in quicksands,
     little by little, much by much, they
are fighting fighting fighting that where
     there was death there may
be life. 'When a man is prey to anger,
he is moved by outside things; when he holds
      his ground in patience patience
       patience, that is action or
      beauty', the soldier's defence
      and hardest armour for

the fight. The world's an orphans' home. Shall
     we never have peace without sorrow?
without pleas of the dying for
    help that won't come? O
quiet form upon the dust, I cannot

look and yet I must. If these great patient
    dyings—all these agonies
        and woundbearings and bloodshed—
    can teach us how to live, these
        dyings were not wasted.

Hate-hardened heart, O heart of iron,
    iron is iron till it is rust.
There never was a war that was
    not inward; I must
fight till I have conquered in myself what
causes war, but I would not believe it.
    I inwardly did nothing.
      O Iscariotlike crime!
    Beauty is everlasting
      And dust is for a time.

MARIANNE MOORE

THE MASSACRE OF THE INNOCENTS

Because I believe in the community of little children,
Because I have suffered such little children to be slain;
I have gazed upon the sunlight, dazed, bewildered,
As is a child by nothing more than rain.

Not until I can no longer climb,
Until my life becomes the tallest tree,
And every limb of it a limb of shame,
Shall I look out in time, in time to see

Again those who were so small they could but die,
Who had only their vast innocence to give,
That I may tell them, pointing down the sky,
How beautiful it might have been to live.

WILLIAM JAY SMITH

A CAROL FOR CHILDREN

God rest you, merry Innocents,
Let nothing you dismay,
Let nothing wound an eager heart
Upon this Christmas day.

Yours be the genial holly wreaths,
The stockings and the tree;
An aged world to you bequeaths
Its own forgotten glee.

Soon, soon enough come crueler gifts,
The anger and the tears;
Between you now there sparsely drifts
A handful yet of years.

Oh, dimly, dimly glows the star
Through the electric throng;
The bidding in temple and bazaar
Drowns out the silver song.

The ancient altars smoke afresh,
The ancient idols stir;
Faint in the reek of burning flesh
Sink frankincense and myrrh.

Gaspar, Balthazar, Melchior!
Where are your offerings now?
What greetings to the Prince of War,
His darkly branded brow?

Two ultimate laws alone we know,
The ledger and the sword—
So far away, so long ago,
We lost the infant Lord.

Only the children clasp his hand;
His voice speaks low to them,
And still for them the shining band
Wings over Bethlehem.

God rest you, merry Innocents,
While innocence endures.
A sweeter Christmas than we to ours
May you bequeath to yours.

OGDEN NASH

151

BAR-ROOM MATINS

Popcorn peanuts clams and gum:
We whose Kingdom has not come
Have mouth like men but still are dumb

Who only deal with Here and Now
As circumstances may allow:
The sponsored programme tells us how.

And yet the preachers tell the pews
What man misuses God can use:
Give us this day our daily news

That we may hear behind the brain
And through the sullen heat's migraine
The atavistic voice of Cain:

'Who entitled you to spy
From your easy heaven? Am I
My brother's keeper? Let him die.'

And God in words we soon forget
Answers through the radio set:
'The curse is on his forehead yet.'

Mass destruction, mass disease:
We thank thee, Lord, upon our knees
That we were born in times like these

When with doom tumbling from the sky
Each of us has an alibi
For doing nothing—Let him die.

Let him die, his death will be
A drop of water in the sea,
A journalist's commodity.

Pretzels crackers chips and beer:
Death is something that we fear
But it titillates the ear.

Anchovy almond ice and gin:
All shall die though none can win;
Let the Untergang begin—

Die the soldiers, die the Jews,
And all the breadless homeless queues.
Give us this day our daily news.

LOUIS MACNEICE

AND THE LORD WAS NOT
IN THE WHIRLWIND

And the Lord was not in the whirlwind.
He sat in the cave looking out and the cave was the world;
Or he sat in his office with in-tray and out-tray
While nobody, nothing, came in but typed memoranda
Although through the curtainless window the wind
                was twirling the gas-drums
And whipping all London away into interstellar negation—
But the Lord was not in the whirlwind.

And the Lord was not in the atom.
He sat in a bar looking in (and the bar was the world)
On a high metal stool between intake and outlet
Still breathing in, breathing out, but nothing and no one
Passed the swing-doors while he waited and watched
                his tumbler erupting
A genie that grew like a mushroom, deleting the
                Words of Creation—
But the Lord was not in the atom.

Yet after all that or before it
As he sat in the cave of his mind (and the cave was the world)
Among old worked flints between insight and hindsight,
Suddenly Something, or Someone, darkened the entrance
But shed a new light on the cave and a still small
                voice on the silence
In spite of ill winds and ill atoms blossomed in pure
                affirmation
Of what lay behind and before it.

LOUIS MACNEICE
From
"Visitations: VII"

THE LITANY OF THE DARK PEOPLE

Our flesh was a battle-ground
Shows now the morning-break;
The ancient deities are downed
For Thy eternal sake.
Now that the past is left behind,
Fling wide Thy garment's hem
To keep us one with Thee in mind,
Thou Christ of Bethlehem.

The thorny wreath may ridge our brow,
The spear may mar our side,
And on white wood from a scented bough
We may be crucified;
Yet no assault the old gods make
Upon our agony
Shall swerve our footsteps from the wake
Of Thine toward Calvary.

And if we hunger now and thirst,
Grant our withholders may,
When heaven's constellations burst
Upon Thy crowning day,
Be fed by us, and given to see
Thy mercy in our eyes,
When Bethlehem and Calvary
Are merged in Paradise.

COUNTEE CULLEN

THE INNUMERABLE CHRIST

Other stars may have their Bethlehem, and their Calvary too.

Professor J. Y. Simpson

Wha kens on whatna Bethlehems
Earth twinkles like a star the nicht,
An' whatna shepherds lift their heids
    In its unearthly licht?

'Yont a' the stars oor een can see
An' farther than their lichts can fly,
I' mony an unco warl' the nicht
    The fatefu' bairnies cry.

I' mony an unco warl' the nicht
The lift gaes black as pitch at noon,
An' sideways on their chests the heids
    O' endless Christs roll doon.

An' when the earth's as cauld's the mune
An' a' its folk are lang syne deid,
On coontless stars the Babe maun cry
    An' the Crucified maun bleed.

HUGH MAC DIARMID

WHEN WILT THOU SAVE THE PEOPLE?

When wilt thou save the people?
   O God of mercy, when?
Not kings and lords, but nations!
   Not thrones and crowns, but men!
Flowers of thy heart, O God, are they;
Let them not pass like weeds away,
Their heritage a sunless day;
     God save the people!

Shall crime bring crime for ever,
   Strength aiding still the strong?
Is it Thy will, O Father,
   That man shall toil for wrong?
"No," say Thy mountains; "No," Thy skies;
Man's clouded sun shall brightly rise,
And songs be heard instead of sighs:
     God save the people!

When wilt thou save the people?
   O God of mercy, when?
The people, Lord, the people,
   Not thrones and crowns, but men!
God save the people; Thine they are,
Thy children, as Thy angels fair;
From vice, oppression, and despair
     God save the people!

EBENEZER ELLIOTT

157

I THINK CONTINUALLY OF THOSE
WHO WERE TRULY GREAT

I think continually of those who were truly great.
Who, from the womb, remembered the soul's history
Through corridors of light where the hours are suns,
Endless and singing. Whose lovely ambition
Was that their lips, still touched with fire,
Should tell of the Spirit, clothed from head to foot
                                        in song.
And who hoarded from the Spring branches
The desires falling across their bodies like blossoms.

What is precious, is never to forget
The essential delight of the blood drawn from ageless
                                        springs
Breaking through rocks in worlds before our earth;
Never to deny its pleasure in the morning simple light,
Nor its grave evening demand for love.
Never to allow gradually the traffic to smother
With noise and fog, the flowering of the Spirit.

Near the snow, near the sun, in the highest fields,
See how these names are fêted by the waving grass
And by the streamers of white cloud
And whispers of wind in the listening sky.
The names of those who in their lives fought for life,
Who wore at their hearts the fire's centre.
Born of the sun, they travelled a short while toward
                                        the sun,
And left the vivid air signed with their honour.

STEPHEN SPENDER

COLOR — CASTE — DENOMINATION

Color—Caste—Denomination—
These—are Time's Affair—
Death's diviner Classifying
Does not know they are—

As in sleep—All Hue forgotten—
Tenets—put behind—
Death's large—Democratic fingers
Rub away the Brand—

If Circassian—He is careless—
If He put away
Chrysalis of Blonde—or Umber—
Equal Butterfly—

They emerge from His Obscuring—
What Death—knows so well—
Our minuter intuitions—
Deem unplausible—

EMILY DICKINSON

BATTLE HYMN OF THE REPUBLIC

Mine eyes have seen the glory of the coming of the Lord;
He is trampling out the vintage where the grapes of wrath
                                    are stored;
He hath loosed the fateful lightning of His terrible swift
                                    sword;
His truth is marching on.
  Glory! Glory! Hallelujah!
  Glory! Glory! Hallelujah!
  Glory! Glory! Hallelujah!
  His truth is marching on.

I have seen Him in the watch fires of a hundred circling
                                    camps
They have builded Him an altar in the evening dews and
                                    damps;
I can read His righteous sentence by the dim and flaring
                                    lamps;
His day is marching on.
  Glory! Glory! Hallelujah!
  Glory! Glory! Hallelujah!
  Glory! Glory! Hallelujah!
  His day is marching on.

He has sounded forth the trumpet that shall never call
                                    retreat;
He is sifting out the hearts of men before His judgment seat;
Oh, be swift, my soul, to answer Him; be jubilant, my feet;
Our God is marching on.
  Glory! Glory! Hallelujah!
  Glory! Glory! Hallelujah!
  Glory! Glory! Hallelujah!
  Our God is marching on.

In the beauty of the lilies Christ was born across the sea,
With a glory in His bosom that transfigures you and me;
As He died to make men holy, let us die to make men free;
While God is marching on.
    Glory! Glory! Hallelujah!
    Glory! Glory! Hallelujah!
    Glory! Glory! Hallelujah!
    While God is marching on.

JULIA WARD HOWE

JERUSALEM

And did those feet in ancient time
 Walk upon England's mountains green?
And was the holy Lamb of God
 On England's pleasant pastures seen?

And did the Countenance Divine
 Shine forth upon our clouded hills?
And was Jerusalem builded here
 Among these dark Satanic Mills?

Bring me my bow of burning gold!
 Bring me my arrows of desire!
Bring me my spear! O clouds, unfold!
 Bring me my chariot of fire!

I will not cease from mental fight,
 Nor shall my sword sleep in my hand,
Till we have built Jerusalem
 In England's green and pleasant land.

WILLIAM BLAKE
From
"Milton"

THE 151st PSALM

Are You looking for us? We are here.
Have You been gathering flowers, Elohim?
We are Your flowers, we have always been.
When will You leave us alone?
We are in America.
We have been here three hundred years.
And what new altar will You deck us with?

Whom are You following, Pillar of Fire?
What barn do you seek shelter in?
At whose gate do You whimper
In this great Palestine?
Whose wages do You take in this New World?
But Israel shall take what it shall take,
Making us ready for Your hungry Hand!

Immigrant God, You follow me;
You go with me, You are a distant tree;
You are the beast that lows in my heart's gates;
You are the dog that follows at my heel;
You are the table on which I lean;
You are the plate from which I eat.

Shepherd of the flocks of praise,
Youth of all youth, ancient of days,
Follow us.

KARL SHAPIRO

163

AMERICA, THE BEAUTIFUL

O beautiful for spacious skies,
For amber waves of grain,
For purple mountain majesties
Above the fruited plain!
America! America!
God shed His grace on thee,
And crown thy good with brotherhood,
From sea to shining sea!

O beautiful for pilgrim feet
Whose stern impassioned stress
A thoroughfare for freedom beat
Across the wilderness!
America! America!
God mend thine ev'ry flaw,
Confirm thy soul in self-control,
Thy liberty in law!

O beautiful for heroes proved
In liberating strife,
Who more than self their country loved,
And mercy more than life!
America! America!
May God thy gold refine,
Till all success be nobleness,
And ev'ry gain divine!

O beautiful for patriot dream
That sees beyond the years
Thine alabaster cities gleam

Undimmed by human tears!
America! America!
God shed His grace on thee,
And crown thy good with brotherhood,
From sea to shining sea!

KATHERINE LEE BATES

WE SHALL OVERCOME

We shall overcome
We shall overcome
We shall overcome some day
O deep in my heart
    I do believe
We shall overcome some day.

The Lord will see us through
The Lord will see us through
The Lord will see us through some day
O deep in my heart
    I do believe
The Lord will see us through some day.

TRADITIONAL AMERICAN

OUR
DAILY
BREAD

THE LORD'S PRAYER

Our Father
which art in heaven,
Hallowed be thy name.
Thy kingdom come.
Thy will be done
In earth, as it is in heaven.
Give us this day our daily bread.
And forgive us our debts,
as we forgive our debtors.
And lead us not into temptation,
but deliver us from evil:
For thine is the kingdom,
and the power, and the glory,
for ever. Amen.

FORGIVE US, O LORD

Forgive us, O lord, we acknowledge ourselves as type of the
common man,

Of the men and women who shut the door and sit by the fire;

Who fear the blessing of God, the loneliness of the night of
God, the surrender required, the deprivation inflicted;
Who fear the injustice of men less than the justice of God;

Who fear the hand at the window, the fire in the thatch, the
fist in the tavern, the push into the canal,

Less than we fear the love of God.

We acknowledge our trespass, our weakness, our fault; we
acknowledge

That the sin of the world is upon our heads; that the blood of
the martyrs and the agony of the saints
Is upon our heads.
Lord, have mercy upon us.
Christ, have mercy upon us.
Lord, have mercy upon us.
Blessed Thomas, pray for us.

T. S. ELIOT
From
"Murder in the Cathedral"

MY PERIOD HAD COME FOR PRAYER

My period had come for Prayer—
No other Art—would do—
My Tactics missed a rudiment—
Creator—Was it you?

God grows above—so those who pray
Horizons—must ascend—
And so I stepped upon the North
To see this Curious Friend—

His House was not—no sign had He—
By chimney—nor by Door
Could I infer his Residence—
Vast Prairies of Air

Unbroken by a Settler—
Were all that I could see—
Infinitude—Had'st Thou no Face
That I might look on Thee?

The Silence condescended—
Creation stopped—for me—
But awed beyond my errand—
I worshipped—did not "pray"—

EMILY DICKINSON

PRAYER

I ask you this:
Which way to go?
I ask you this:
Which sin to bear?
Which crown to put
Upon my hair?
I do not know,
Lord God,
I do not know.

LANGSTON HUGHES

EASTWARD I STAND, MERCIES I BEG

Eastward I stand,   mercies I beg:
bid I the glorious Domine,   bid I the mighty Ruler
bid I the holy   Keeper of the heavenly kingdom,
the earth I bid   and heaven above,
and in truth   Sancta Maria,
and the might of heaven   and the high vault.
that I may this spell   through the gift of the Lord
undo with my teeth   through firm thanks;
awaken these fruits   for our earthly use,
fill the earth   with fast belief,
beautify the proud fields,   as the page said:
that he had mercy on earth   who gloriously
gave alms,   in accordance with the thought of the Lord.
      Erce, erce, erce,   mother of earth,
      May the Elder grant,   the eternal Lord,
      fields waxing   and flourishing,
      increasing   and gaining in strength:
      Shafts of millet,   bright fruits
      and the broad   crops of barley
      and the white   crops of wheat,
      and all   crops of the earth.
Grant him   eternal Lord
and his holy ones   who are in heaven,
that his crop be in peace   and be saved from
every fiend   and every evil
and from the witchcraft   sown throughout the land.
Now I bid the Ruler   who shaped the earth
that there be no wife so talkative   no man so crafty
that they may upset   the words which have been spoken.

*From an
Anglo-Saxon charm
Translated by
Sarah Plotz*

FOR THE EARTH GOD

Thy need is great
And great our need to sing,
For days of trouble are upon us.
The bullock of Abomey
Says to him in Cana,
It is the day of our trouble;
The carrier of grain
Says to the bearer of salt,
Thy load is heavy, brother.
And this is the day for carrying;
The bearer of the dead
Says to the carrier of ladders,
It is the day for carrying loads,
It is the day of trouble.

DAHOMEAN SONG
Translated by
Frances Herskovits

COMFORT YE, COMFORT YE MY PEOPLE

1 Comfort ye, comfort ye my people, saith your God.
2 Speak ye comfortably to Jerusalem, and cry unto her, that
    her warfare is accomplished, that her iniquity is
    pardoned: for she hath received of the LORD's hand
        double of all her sins.
3 The voice of him that crieth in the wilderness, Prepare ye
    the way of the LORD, make straight in the desert a
        highway for our God.
4 Every valley shall be exalted, and every mountain and hill
    shall be made low; and the crooked shall be made
        straight, and the rough places plain:
5 And the glory of the LORD shall be revealed, and all flesh
    shall see it together: for the mouth of the LORD hath
        spoken it.
6 The voice said, Cry. And he said, What shall I cry? All
    flesh is grass, and all the goodliness thereof is as the
        flower of the field:
7 The grass withereth, the flower fadeth; because the spirit
    of the LORD bloweth upon it: surely the people is grass.
8 The grass withereth, the flower fadeth: but the word of
        our God shall stand forever.
9 O Zion, that bringest good tidings, get thee up into a high
    mountain; O Jerusalem, that bringest good tidings,
    lift up thy voice with strength; lift it up, be not
    afraid; say unto the cities of Judah, Behold
        your God!
10 Behold, the Lord God will come with strong hand, and
    his arm shall rule for him: behold, his reward is
        with him, and his work before him.
11 He shall feed his flock like a shepherd: he shall gather the
    lambs with his arm and carry them in his bosom,
        and shall gently lead those that are young.

ISAIAH 40:1-11

OLD SHEPHERD'S PRAYER

Up to the bed by the window, where I be lyin',
Comes bells and bleats of the flock wi' they two
                              children's clack.
Over, from under the eaves there's the starlings
                              flyin',
And down in yard, fit to burst his chain, yapping
          out at Sue I do hear young Mac.

Turning around like a falled-over sack
I can see team ploughin' in Whithy-bush field and
    meal carts startin' up road to Church-Town;
Saturday arternoon the men goin' back
And the women from market, trapin' home over the down.

Heavenly Master, I wud like to wake to they same
                              green places
Where I be know'd for breakin' dogs and follerin'
                              sheep.
And if I may not walk in th' old ways and look on
                              th' old faces
I wud sooner sleep.

                                        CHARLOTTE MEW

STONE TOO CAN PRAY

Lord, Lord—these miracles, the streets, all say—
bring to us soon thy best, most golden day,
that every stick and stone for thee may shine,
they praise be sung in every shaft and line.

Lord, Lord—the steeples and the towers cry—
deepen beyond belief thy ancient sky,
deeper than time or terror be that blue
and we'll still praise thee by still pointing true.

Lord, Lord—the fountains weep—hear our delight,
these waters for birds and children we keep bright;
where children shout, and the stone dolphin sings,
bless with they rainbow these holy eyes and wings.

Lord, Lord—all voices say, and all together,
stone, steel, and waking man, and waking weather—
give us thy day, that once more we may be
the endless miracle that embodies thee.

CONRAD AIKEN

LINES WRITTEN IN HER BREVIARY

Let nothing disturb thee,
Nothing affright thee;
All things are passing;
God never changeth;
Patient endurance
Attaineth to all things;
Who God possesseth
In nothing is wanting;
Alone God sufficeth.

SAINT THERESA
Translated by
Henry Wadsworth Longfellow

PRAYER IN MID-PASSAGE

O Thou my monster, Thou my guide,
Be with me where the bluffs divide
Nor let me contemplate return
To where by backward chattels burn
In haunts of friendship and untruth—
The Cities of the Plain of Youth.

O pattern of inhuman good,
Hard critic of our thought and blood,
By whose decree there is no zone
Where man can live by men alone,
Unveil Thyself that all may see
Thy fierce impersonality.

We were the past—and doomed because
We were a past that never was;
Yet grant to men that they may climb
This time-bound ladder out of time
And by our human organs we
Shall thus transcend humanity.

Take therefore, though Thou disregard,
This prayer, this hymn, this feckless word,
O Thou my silence, Thou my song,
To whom all focal doubts belong
And but for whom this breath were breath—
Thou my meaning, Thou my death.

LOUIS MACNEICE

EARTH AND SKY

O potent Earth, and Heaven god-built,—
  Of Heaven are god and man begot,
  And Earth brings forth to mortal lot
Fruits of the rain from Heaven spilt—

The grass she bears and wild things' breed:
  All-Mother rightly is her name.
  To Earth go back from Earth who came,
And what was born from skyey seed

Travels again to Heaven's field.
  There's nothing dies of all that's born;
  But one by other toss'd and torn
Old things are changed, and new revealed.

EURIPIDES
Translated by
C. M. Bowra

FOR ALL SORTS AND CONDITIONS

O love of God, God's love, love that alone
Gives hate its meaning, and gives argument
　　To men, who out of grief and a rent
　　Heart, looking on the world's pain,
　　Rend from their hearts belief
In all that lends authority to grief,
Euclidizing one and one and one
　　To nowt but a nowt—
Have mercy on all who will not accept Thy mercy,
　　Who gouge their eyes out
　　Because they cannot see;
　　Then call their darkness—Thee.

NORMAN NICHOLSON

PRAYER
(After St. Theresa of Avila)

Have pity on us, Power just and severe,
   Have pity on our greed, our hate, our lust,
And on our unending anxieties, our ugly fear.
   Great Wisdom, grant wisdom to this timid dust.

Have patience with us, who have betrayed one another
   And parted the single and seamless robe of man,
And divided his garments among us, who is our brother.
   Infinite Patience, have patience if You can.

Have mercy on us—because we are merciless
   And have need of mercy we are not worthy of—
And on our angry littleness,
   Pity Inexorable, Remorseless Love.

JOHN HALL WHEELOCK

THREE ELEMENTS

Three elements,
Earth, water, and fire. I have passed through them all,
Still to find no Elysium for my hands,
Still to find no Elysium but growth,
And the slow will to grow to match my task.

Three elements. I have not sought the fourth
Deeply, till now—the element of air,
The everlasting element of God,
Who must be there in spite of all we see,
Who must be there in spite of all we bear,
Who must exist where all Elysiums
Are less than shadows of a hunter's fire,
Lighted at night to scare a wolf away.

I know the wolf—his scars are in my hide
And no Elysiums can rub them out.
Therefore at last, I lift my hands to You
Who Were and Are and Must Be, if our world
Is anything but a lost ironclad
Shipped with a crew of fools and mutineers
To drift between the cold forts of the stars.

STEPHEN VINCENT BENÉT
Abraham Lincoln's Prayer
From "John Brown's Body"

TO DESTINY

Bear down lightly,
O my load,
Bear down lightly
As the boat touches the water;
Bear down lightly,
O my load
For the boat is near to sinking;
Bear lightly,
And I will make offerings
To the Master of Destiny.

DAHOMEAN SONG
Translated by
Frances Herskovits

GOD LEADS THE WAY

Lead me, O God, and thou my Destiny,
To that one place which you will have me fill.
I follow gladly. Should I strive with Thee,—
A recreant, I needs must follow still.

CLEANTHES
Translated by
C. C. Martindale

185

THE CHILD

The child is holy and most wise;
within the Wall he plays;
he sees the watchers in the skies;
he knows the hidden ways.

For those within the pentagram
see not as others see;
they know in every lamb the Lamb;
the Tree in every tree.

But those who pass beyond the Pale
at evening eye the west
and feel the swords of sunset flail
the evil in the breast.

May we again as children dwell,
nor fear the wheeling flame;
knowing the ways of Wisdom well
and in all names, the Name.

IVOR POPHAM

GOD BE IN MY HEAD

God be in my head
And in my Understanding.

God be in my eyes
And in my Looking.

God be in my mouth
And in my Speaking.

God be in my heart
And in my Thinking.

God be at mine end
And at my Departing.

ANONYMOUS

LORD – THINE THE DAY

Lord—Thine the day,
And I the day's.

DAG HAMMARSKJÖLD
Translated by
Leif Sjöberg and W. H. Auden

I WILL BOW AND BE SIMPLE

I will bow and be simple
I will bow and be free
I will bow and be humble
Yea bow like the willow-tree
I will bow this is the token
I will wear the easy yoke
I will bow and be broken
Yea I'll fall upon the rock.

TRADITIONAL AMERICAN
North family
New Lebanon (?) Shakers

CRADLE SONG

O my deir hert, young Jesus sweit,
Prepare thy creddil in my spreit,
And I sall rock thee in my hert
And never mair from thee depart.

But I sall praise thee evermoir
With sangis sweit unto thy gloir;
The knees of my hert sall I bow,
And sing that richt *Balulalow!*

ANONYMOUS

SAINT FRANCIS AND
SAINT BENEDIGHT

Saint Francis and Saint Benedight
blesse this house from wicked wight,
From the nightmare and the goblin
that is hight Goodefellow Robin,
Keep it from all Evil spirites,
Fayries, wezles, bats, and ferryts,
From curfew time to the next prime.

ANONYMOUS

A CHILD'S GRACE

Here a little child I stand
Heaving up my either hand;
Cold as paddocks though they be,
Here I lift them up to Thee,
For a benison to fall
On our meat and on us all. Amen.

ROBERT HERRICK

LITTLE CATKINS

Little boys and little maidens
Little candles, little catkins
    Homeward bring.

Little lights are burning softly,
People cross themselves in passing—
    Scent of spring.

Little wind so bold and merry,
Little raindrops, don't extinguish
    These flames, pray!

I will rise tomorrow, early,
Rise to greet you, Willow Sunday,
    Holy day.

ALEXANDER BLOK
Translated by
Babette Deutsch

KIBBUTZ SABBATH

Modest and needy is my destiny in thy world, O God!
The destiny of them that cut the wood and draw the water.
Nameless I am, one of the Gibeonites,
The eternal menials of thy temple in Jerusalem.

And, as the sun sets, I perform the oblation.
I bathe my body and dress it in white shirt.
I sit down as brother to the rest of the priestly household
And receive my portion from off the table of the shewbread.

I sit as a Levite among Levites,
Who in holiness lift up to thee a song of praise.
O Lord! I thank thee for the goodness of growth,
I thank thee for the slice of bread and the prayerful mood.

LEVI BEN AMITTAI
Translated by
Simon Halkin

INVOCATION
Hasidic Song

Good morning to you, Lord of the world!
I, Levi Isaac, son of Sarah of Berditshev, am coming to you in
      a legal matter concerning your people of Israel.
What do you want of Israel?
It is always: Command the children of Israel!
It is always: Speak unto the children of Israel!
Merciful Father! How many peoples are there in the world?
Persians, Babylonians, Edomites!
The Russians—what do they say?
   Our emperor is the emperor!
The Germans—what do they say?
   Our kingdom is the kingdom!
The English—what do they say?
   Our kingdom is the kingdom!
But I, Levi Isaac, son of Sarah of Berditshev, say:
   "Glorified and sanctified be His great name!"
And I, Levi Isaac, son of Sarah of Berditshev, say:
I shall not go hence, nor budge from my place
until there be a finish
until there be an end of exile—
"Glorified and sanctified be His great name!"

LEVI ISAAC OF BERDITSHEV
Translated by
Olga Marx

O SING UNTO THE LORD
A NEW SONG

O sing unto the Lord a new song; for he hath done marvelous
    things: his right hand, and his holy arm, hath gotten
                  him the victory.
The Lord hath made known his salvation: his righteousness
    hath he openly showed in the sight of the heathen.
He hath remembered his mercy and his truth toward the
    house of Israel: all the ends of the earth have seen
            the salvation of our God.
Make a joyful noise unto the Lord, all the earth: make a loud
        noise, and rejoice, and sing praise.
Sing unto the Lord with the harp; with the harp, and the
        voice of a psalm.
With trumpets and sound of cornet make a joyful noise
      before the Lord, the King.
Let the sea roar, and the fulness thereof; the world, and they
      that dwell therein.
Let the floods clap their hands: let the hills be joyful together
Before the Lord; for he cometh to judge the earth: with
    righteousness shall he judge the world, and
        the people with equity.

THE NINETY-EIGHTH PSALM

I THANK YOU GOD FOR MOST
THIS AMAZING

i thank You God for most this amazing
day:for the leaping greenly spirits of trees
and a blue true dream of sky;and for everything
which is natural which is infinite which is yes

(i who have died am alive again today,
and this is the sun's birthday;this is the birth
day of life and love and wings:and of the gay
great happening illimitably earth)

how should tasting touching hearing seeing
breathing any—lifted from the no
of all nothing—human merely being
doubt unimaginable You?

(now the ears of my ears awake and
now the eyes of my eyes are opened)

e. e. cummings

HYMN

The words of hymns abruptly plod
In dark simplicity,
Telling of yearning after God.
And is it God with me?

Yearning like this can only go
To lines compressed and grim.
With slow surprise I come to know
The reason for a hymn.

Love is a seeking and a thirst
And has no ready speech.
That glib perfection known at first
My hymn can never reach.

Blessed are they which hunger and thirst
To thirst is to be filled;
Better that leaves and sunlit water
Should never quite be stilled.

Can only God contain the whole,
And compass every part?
Oh, love, take all the faithfulness
Of my unfaithful heart!

LOUISE TOWNSEND NICHOLL

WMFFRE THE SWEEP

(Cyhydedd Naw Ban)

Wmffre the Sweep was mad as a mink,
Covered with cinders, blacker than ink.
Didn't mind darkness, didn't mind stink;
Light was his loathing, light made him blink
Coming through crevices, cranny or chink.
Drank through his whiskers, dust in his drink.

Wretched the ways of Wmffre the Sweep:
Little to gain, and nothing to keep;
Labor was plenty, labor was cheap,
Filthy the flues, and chimneys were steep;
Grimy, red-eyed, unable to weep,
Home to his pallet, ugly in sleep.

Wmffre the Sweep beheld a strange sight
In his day's dark or in the real night:
Ninety-nine angels, harnessed in light,
Michael among them, bearded and bright,
Majesty moving, melody, might—
Wmffre the Sweep was inspired to write.

Wmffre the Sweep, a lout and a clod,
Fed all his life on cabbage and cod.
Housed in a hovel, never well-shod,
Shouldering buckets, besoms and hod,
Shovelled, like all men, under the sod,
Left a great poem, praise of his God.

ROLFE HUMPHRIES

LORD, THOU HAST BEEN
OUR DWELLING PLACE

Lord, thou hast been our dwelling place in all generations.
Before the mountains were brought forth, or ever thou hadst
formed the earth and the world, even from everlasting
to everlasting, thou art God.
Thou turnest men to destruction and sayest, Return, ye
children of men.
For a thousand years in thy sight are but as yesterday when it
is past, and as a watch in the night.
Thou carriest them away as with a flood; they are as a sleep:
in the morning they are like grass which groweth up.
In the morning it flourisheth, and groweth up; in the evening
it is cut down, and withereth.
For we are consumed by thine anger, and by thy wrath are
we troubled.
Thou hast set our iniquities before thee, our secret sins in the
light of thy countenance.
For all our days are passed away in thy wrath: we spend our
years as a tale that is told.
The days of our years are threescore and ten; and if by reason
of strength they be fourscore years, yet is their
strength labour and sorrow; for it is soon cut
off, and we fly away.
Who knoweth the power of thine anger? even according to
thy fear, so is thy wrath.
So teach us to number our days, that we may apply our hearts
unto wisdom.
Return, O Lord, how long? and let it repent thee concerning
thy servants.
O satisfy us early with thy mercy; that we may rejoice and be
glad all our days.
Make us glad according to the days wherein thou hast afflicted
us, and the years wherein we have seen evil.

Let thy work appear unto thy servants, and thy glory unto
their children.
And let the beauty of the Lord our God be upon us: and
establish thou the work of our hands upon us;
yea, the work of our hands establish thou it.

THE NINETIETH PSALM

ADON 'OLAM
(Lord of the World)

The Lord of all, who reigned supreme
　　Ere first Creation's form was framed;
When all was finished by His will
　　His Name Almighty was proclaimed.

He is my God and Savior too,
　　To whom I turn in sorrow's hour—
My banner proud, my refuge sure—
　　Who hears and answers with His power.

Then in His hand myself I lay,
　　And trusting sleep: and wake with cheer;
My soul and body are His care:
　　The Lord doth guard, I have no fear!

Translated by
F. De Sola Mendes
From the Hebrew

199

O GOD, OUR HELP IN AGES PAST

O God, our help in ages past,
Our hope for years to come;
Our shelter from the stormy blast,
And our eternal home.

Under the shadow of Thy throne
Thy Saints have dwelt secure;
Sufficient is Thine arm alone,
And our defense is sure.

Before the hills in order stood,
Or earth received her frame,
From everlasting Thou art God,
To endless years the same.

A thousand ages in Thy sight
Are like an evening gone;
Short as the watch that ends the night
Before the rising sun.

Time, like an ever-rolling stream,
Bears all its sons away;
They fly, forgotten as a dream
Dies at the opening day.

O God, our help in ages past,
Our hope for years to come;
Be Thou our guide while life shall last,
And our eternal home.

ISAAC WATTS

FOR THE BICENTENARY OF
ISAAC WATTS
Died 25th November 1748

Life was a narrow lobby, dark,
Railed in with pain; the windows gave
This side on a padlocked park,
That side on an open grave.

But God looked through the skylight; hell
Was six feet down below the ground.
The cellar had a smoky smell;
The wind had a Mosaic sound.

A voice rang out; the organ pealed
Fit to blow the roof off. Stars
Were stacked in Heaven's harvest field,
And halt and hobbled dragged the cars.

NORMAN NICHOLSON

A SONG FOR SIMEON

Lord, the Roman hyacinths are blooming in bowls and
The winter sun creeps by the snow hills;
The stubborn season has made stand.
My life is light, waiting for the death wind,
Like a feather on the back of my hand.
Dust in sunlight and memory in corners
Wait for the wind that chills towards the dead land.

Grant us thy peace.
I have walked many years in this city,
Kept faith and fast, provided for the poor,
Have given and taken honour and ease.
There went never any rejected from my door.
Who shall remember my house, where shall live my
                              children's children
When the time of sorrow is come?
They will take to the goat's path, and the fox's home,
Fleeing from the foreign faces and the foreign swords.

Before the time of cords and scourges and lamentation
Grant us thy peace.
Before the stations of the mountain of desolation,
Before the certain hour of maternal sorrow,
Now at this birth season of decease,
Let the Infant, the still unspeaking and unspoken Word,
Grant Israel's consolation
To one who has eighty years and no to-morrow.

According to thy word.
They shall praise Thee and suffer in every generation
With glory and derision,
Light upon light, mounting the saints' stair.
Not for me the martyrdom, the ecstasy of thought and prayer,

Not for me the ultimate vision.
Grant me thy peace.
(And a sword shall pierce thy heart,
Thine also.)
I am tired with my own life and the lives of those after me,
I am dying in my own death and the deaths of those after me.
Let thy servant depart,
Having seen thy salvation.

T. S. ELIOT

I WONDER AS I WANDER

I wonder as I wander
    Out under the sky
How Jesus, the Saviour
    Did come for to die
For poor ornery people
    Like you and like I.
I wonder as I wander
    Out under the sky.

When Mary birthed Jesus
    'Twas in a cow's stall
With wise men and farmers
    And shepherds and all.
But high from God's heaven
    A star's light did fall
And the promise of ages
    It then did recall.
I wonder as I wander
    Out under the sky.

If Jesus had wanted for
    Any wee thing
A star in the sky or a bird
    On the wing
Or all of God's angels in
    Heaven for to sing
He surely could have it
    'Cause he was the King!
I wonder as I wander
    Out under the sky.

TRADITIONAL AMERICAN
(John Jacob Niles)

THE SHEPHERD BOY SINGS
IN THE VALLEY OF HUMILIATION

He that is down needs fear no fall,
  He that is low, no pride;
He that is humble ever shall
  Have God to be his guide.

I am content with what I have,
  Little be it or much:
And, Lord, contentment still I crave,
  Because Thou savest such.

Fullness to such a burden is
  That go on pilgrimage:
Here little, and hereafter bliss,
  Is best from age to age.

JOHN BUNYAN

A HYMNE TO GOD THE FATHER

Wilt thou forgive that sinne where I begunne,
   Which was my sin, though it were done before?
Wilt thou forgive those sinnes through which I runne,
   And doe them still: though still I doe deplore?
     When thou hast done, though hast not done,
      For I have more.

Wilt thou forgive that sinne which I have wonne
   Others to sinne? and, made my sinne their doore?
Wilt thou forgive that sinne which I did shunne
   A yeare, or two: but wallowed in, a score?
     When thou hast done, thou hast not done,
      For I have more.

I have a sinne of feare, that when I have spunne
   My last thred, I shall perish on the shore;
Sweare by thy selfe, that at my death thy Sonne
   Shall shine as he shines now, and heretofore;
     And having done that, thou hast done,
      I feare no more.

                 JOHN DONNE

THE RIBS AND TERRORS
IN THE WHALE

The ribs and terrors in the whale,
   Arched over me a dismal gloom,
While all God's sun-lit waves rolled by,
   And lift me deepening down to doom.

I saw the opening maw of hell,
   With endless pains and sorrows there;
Which none but they that feel can tell—
   Oh, I was plunging to despair.

In black distress, I called my God,
   When I could scarce believe him mine,
He bowed his ear to my complaints—
   No more the whale did me confine.

With speed he flew to my relief,
   As on a radiant dolphin borne;
Awful, yet bright, as lightning shone
   The face of my Deliverer God.

My song forever shall record
   That terrible, that joyful hour;
I give the glory to my God,
   His all the mercy and the power.

HERMAN MELVILLE

MARINERS' CAROL

So still the night swinging,
   Wind of our faring,
Only the bows' seethe to lap us,
Stays and wake whispering,
The thin bell striking,
And our hearts in their blindness.
   O star, shine before us!

The serpent's deep sliding,
   Wind of our faring,
Is everywhere around us,
Heaves under us, gliding;
We know its toothed curling
The whole world encircles.
   O star, shine before us!

Crushed in its drag and keeping,
   Wind of our faring,
The darkened dead have no peace,
World-without-end shifting;
All, all are there, and no resting.
It exults above their faces.
   O star, shine before us!

The horizon's perfect ring,
  Wind of our faring,
None enters nor ever has.
And we, like a cradle, rocking:
For the first glimpse of our homing
We roll and are restless.
  O star, shine before us!

Till, heaven and earth joining,
  Wind of our faring,
  It is born to us
Like the first line of dawn breaking;
For that word and sight yearning
We keep the long watches.
  O star, shine before us!

W. S. MERWIN

LIGHT SHINING OUT OF DARKNESS

God moves in a mysterious way,
   His wonders to perform;
He plants his footsteps in the sea,
   And rides upon the storm.

Deep in unfathomable mines
   Of never-failing skill,
He treasures up his bright designs,
   And works his sovereign will.

Ye fearful saints fresh courage take,
   The clouds ye so much dread
Are big with mercy, and shall break
   In blessing on your head.

Judge not the Lord by feeble sense
   But trust him for his grace;
Behind a frowning providence,
   He hides a smiling face.

His purposes will ripen fast,
   Unfolding ev'ry hour;
The bud may have a bitter taste,
   But sweet will be the flow'r.

Blind unbelief is sure to err,
   And scan his work in vain;
God is his own interpreter,
   And he will make it plain.

WILLIAM COWPER

THE SPACIOUS FIRMAMENT ON HIGH

The Spacious Firmament on high,
With all the blue Ethereal Sky,
And spangled Heav'ns, a Shining Frame,
Their great Original proclaim:
Th'unwearied Sun, from day to day,
Does his Creator's Pow'r display,
And publishes to every Land
The Work of an Almighty Hand.

Soon as the Evening Shades prevail,
The Moon takes up the wondrous Tale,
And nightly to the list'ning Earth
Repeats the Story of her Birth:
Whilst all the Stars that round her burn,
And all the Planets, in their turn,
Confirm the Tidings as they rowl,
And spread the Truth from Pole to Pole.

What though, in solemn Silence, all
Move round the dark terrestrial Ball?
What tho' nor real Voice nor Sound
Amid their radiant Orbs be found?
In Reason's Ear they all rejoice,
And utter forth a glorious Voice,
For ever singing, as they shine,
The Hand that made us is Divine.

JOSEPH ADDISON

HYMN

Lord, by whose breath all souls and seeds are living
  With life that is and life that is to be,
First-fruits of earth we offer with thanksgiving
  For fields in flood with summer's golden sea.

Lord of the earth, accept these gifts in token
  Thou in thy works are to be all-adored,
From whom the light as daily bread is broken,
  Sunset and dawn as wine and milk are poured.

Poor is our praise, but these shall be our psalter;
  Lo, like thyself they rose up from the dead;
Lord, give them back when at thy holy altar
  We feed on thee, who are the living bread.

ANDREW YOUNG

A MIGHTY FORTRESS IS OUR GOD

A mighty fortress is our God,
A bulwark never failing,
Our helper He, amid the flood
Of mortal ill prevailing;
For still our ancient foe
Doth seek to work us woe,
His craft and power are great,
And armed with cruel hate,
On earth is not his equal.

MARTIN LUTHER
Translated by
F. H. Hedge

THE EARTH IS THE LORD'S

The earth is the Lord's, and the fulness thereof; the world,
      and they that dwell therein.
For he hath founded it upon the seas, and established it
      upon the floods.
Who shall ascend into the hill of the Lord? or who shall
      stand in his holy place?
He that hath clean hands, and a pure heart; who hath not
     lifted up his soul unto vanity, nor sworn
        deceitfully.
He shall receive the blessing from the Lord, and righteousness
     from the God of his salvation.
This is the generation of them that seek him, that seek thy
      face, O Jacob. Selah.
Lift up your heads, O ye gates; and be ye lifted up, ye
     everlasting doors; and the King of glory
       shall come in.
Who is this king of glory? The Lord strong and mighty, the
      Lord mighty in battle.
Lift up your heads, O ye gates; even lift them up, ye
     everlasting doors; and the King of glory
       shall come in.
Who is this King of glory? The Lord of Hosts, he is the
      King of glory. Selah.

         THE TWENTY-FOURTH PSALM

Index of Authors

Abrahams, Israel (translator), 48
Addison, Joseph, 211
Aiken, Conrad, 177
American Spiritual, 97, 101
American Traditional, 165, 188, 204
Anonymous, 16, 100, 139, 187, 189
Arnold, Matthew, 78
Auden, W. H., 61
Auden, W. H. (translator), 188
Bates, Katherine Lee, 164
Benét, Stephen Vincent, 183
Betjeman, John, 12
Bishop, John Peale, 90, 110
Blake, William, 18, 19, 162
Blok, Alexander, 191
Bowra, C. M. (translator), 180
Brontë, Emily, 4
Bunyan, John, 205
Bynner, Witter, 3, 83
Campbell, Roy, 21
Cleanthes, 185
Clough, Arthur Hugh, 121
Coleridge, Mary, 74, 99
Cowper, William, 210
Crane, Stephen, 72
Cullen, Countee, 155
cummings, e. e., 195
Day Lewis, C., 29, 42, 82, 135
de la Mare, Walter, 20, 83
Deutsch, Babette (translator), 55, 56, 98, 191
Dickinson, Emily, 10, 71, 91, 159, 171
Donne, John, 52, 58, 206
Drummond, William, 106
Eberhart, Richard, 77, 133
Eliot, T. S., 26, 170, 202

Elliott, Ebenezer, 157
Emerson, Ralph Waldo, 23
Euripides, 70, 180
Fitzgerald, Edward (translator), 40, 66
Frost, Robert, 35, 40
Garrett, George, 118
Graves, Robert, 105
Gregory, Horace, 111
Gunn, Thom, 31
Halkin, Simon (translator), 192
Hammarskjöld, Dag, 188
Hardy, Thomas, 65, 128
Headlam, Walter (translator), 5
Hedge, F. H. (translator), 213
Herbert, George, 44, 51, 92
Herrick, Robert, 190
Herskovits, Frances (translator), 25, 174, 184
Hillyer, Robert (translator), 24
Hodgson, Ralph, 131
Hopkins, Gerard Manley, 88, 124, 129, 134
Housman, A. E., 87
Howe, Julia Ward, 160
Hughes, Langston, 172
Hughes, Ted, 86, 127
Humphries, Rolfe, 197
Johnson, James Weldon, 132
Khayyám, Omar, 40, 66
Kirkup, James, 22, 47, 91
Knight, John, 33
Levi Ben Amittai, 192
Levi Isaac of Berditshev, 193
Longfellow, Henry Wadsworth (translator), 178
Luther, Martin, 213
Macdiarmid, Hugh, 156
McGinley, Phyllis, 108, 109

Macleish, Archibald, 69
MacNeice, Louis, 41, 84, 152,
  154, 179
Markham, Edwin, 142
Martindale, C. C. (translator),
  185
Marx, Olga (translator), 193
Masters, Edgar Lee, 85
Melville, Herman, 207
Mendes, F. De Sola
  (translator), 199
Merton, Thomas, 14
Merwin, W. S., 208
Mew, Charlotte, 176
Milton, John, 76
Moore, Marianne, 138, 146
Muir, Edwin, 13, 72
Nash, Ogden, 150
Nemerov, Howard, 123
Nicholl, Louise Townsend, 196
Nicholson, Norman, 57, 181, 201
Pindar, 5
Pitter, Ruth, 141
Plotz, Sarah (translator), 173
Polonsky, Yakov, 17
Popham, Ivor, 186
Pushkin, Alexander, 98
Rich, Adrienne Cecile, 75, 107
Ridler, Anne, 11
Rilke, Rainer Maria, 55, 56
Robinson, Edwin Arlington, 89

Roethke, Theodore, 46
Sarton, May, 116
Sassoon, Siegfried, 8
Sewell, Elizabeth, 38, 104
Shakespeare, William, 53
Shapiro, Karl, 102, 163
Sitwell, Edith, 144
Sjoberg, Leif (translator), 188
Smart, Christopher, 97
Smith, William Jay, 149
Solomon Ibn Gabirol, 48
Spender, Stephen, 158
Stephens, James, 130
Symonds, J. A. (translator), 70
Taylor, Edward, 49
Tennyson, Alfred, 81, 136
Theresa, 178
Thomas, Dylan, 60
Thompson, Francis, 7
Updike, John, 36
Van Doren, Mark, 80, 122, 126
Vaughan, Henry, 9
Villa, José Garcia, 50, 54
Watkins, Vernon, 6
Watts, Isaac, 200
Wheelock, John Hall, 182
Wilbur, Richard, 45, 124
Wordsworth, William, 59
Yeats, William Butler, 28, 114
Young, Andrew, 212
Zangwill, Israel (translator), 100

Index of Titles

A Mighty Fortress Is Our God, 213

Adon 'Olam, 199

After Reading Certain Books, 74

America, the Beautiful, 164

And Death Shall Have No Dominion, 60

And the Lord Was Not in the Whirlwind, 154

Angels Came A-Mustering, The, 100

Antichrist, 72

As Kingfishers Catch Fire, 134

At the Grave of Henry Vaughan, 8

At the Round Earth's Imagined Corners, Blow, 58

Ballad of Father Gilligan, The, 114

Bar-Room Matins, 152

Batter My Heart, Three Person'd God, 52

Battle Hymn of the Republic, 160

Beauteous, Yea Beauteous More Than These, 97

Bells of Heaven, The, 131

Blinded Bird, The, 128

Book of Kells, The, 123

Brahma, 23

Burning Bush, The, 57

But God's Own Descent, 35

Carol for Children, A, 150

Cat and Mouse, 127

Child, The, 186

Child's Grace, A, 190

Chiliasm, 77

Christmas Eve, 29

Christmas Sonnet, A, 89

Collar, The, 92

Color—Caste—Denomination, 159

Comfort Ye, Comfort Ye My People, 175

Conversation in Avila, 108

Cosmic Fabric, The, 17

Cradle Song, 189

Crag Jack's Apostasy, 86

Creditor, The, 41

Curse God and Die, You Said to Me, 69

Didymus, 84

Dirge for the New Sunrise, 144

Donkey, 126

Dover Beach, 78

Earth and Sky, 180

Earth Is The Lord's, The, 214

Easter Hymn, 87

Eastward I Stand, Mercies I Beg, 173

Eternity's Low Voice, 122

False Gods, 83

Father to the Man, 33

For All Sorts and Conditions, 181

For the Bicentenary of Isaac Watts, 201

For the Earth God, 174

Foreigner Comes to Earth on Boston Common, A, 111

Forgiveness, 38

Forgive, O Lord, My Little Jokes on Thee, 40

Forgive Us, O Lord, 170

Francis Jammes: A Prayer to Go to Paradise with the Donkeys, 124

From Thee to Thee, 48

Giver of Life, The, 25

Giving and Taking, 47

Go Down, Moses, 101
God Be in My Head, 187
God, Is, Like, Scissors, 50
God Leads the Way, 185
Great Magicians, The, 82
Guest, The, 16
Hap, 65
He Is Like the Lotus, 24
He Is the Way, 61
Huswifery, 49
Hymn, 196
Hymn, 212
Hymne to God the Father, A, 206
I Need No Sky, 3
i thank You God for most this amazing, 195
I Think Continually of Those Who Were Truly Great, 158
I Will Bow and Be Simple, 188
I Wonder as I Wander, 204
In a Dark Time, 46
In Distrust of Merits, 146
In the Wilderness, 105
Innumerable Christ, The, 156
Invocation, 193
Jerusalem, 162
Jesus and His Mother, 31
Job, 104
Journey of the Magi, 26
Kibbutz Sabbath, 192
Kingdom of God, The, 7
Lamb, The, 18
Life after Death, 5
Light Shining Out of Darkness, 210
Lines Written in Her Breviary, 178
Litany of the Dark People, The, 155
Little Catkins, 191
Little Things, 130

Lord—Thine the Day, 188
Lord, Thou Hast Been Our Dwelling Place, 198
Lord's Prayer, The, 169
Lucifer in the Train, 75
Lyke-Wake Dirge, A, 139
Man is God's Nature, 133
Man with the Hoe, The, 142
Mariner's Carol, 208
Massacre of the Innocents, The, 149
Murder of Moses, The, 102
My, Fellowship, With, God, 50
My Period Had Come for Prayer, 171
Myself When Young Did Eagerly Frequent, 66
My Soul is Weary of My Life, 67
Nature of Love, The, 91
No Coward Soul Is Mine, 4
O God, Our Help in Ages Past, 200
Of God We Ask One Favor, 71
Oh Thou, Who Man of Baser Earth Didst Make, 40
Oh Yet We Trust that Somehow Good, 81
Old Gods, The, 13
Old Shepherd's Prayer, 176
151st Psalm, The, 163
O Sing Unto the Lord a New Song, 194
Our Birth Is But a Sleep and a Forgetting, 59
Peace, 98
Pied Beauty, 124
Poor Soul, the Center of My Sinful Earth, 53
Praise Doubt, 80
Prayer, 83
Prayer, 172

Prayer (After St. Theresa of
Avila), 182
Prayer in Mid-Passage, 179
Proof, The, 45
Prophet, The, 98
Pulley, The, 51
Redemption, 44
Revivalist in Boston, A, 107
Ribs and Terrors in the Whale,
The, 207
Saint Francis, 110
Saint Francis and Saint
Benedight, 189
Saint John the Baptist, 106
Saints, 117
Santos: New Mexico, 116
Say Not the Struggle Naught
Availeth, 121
Second Coming, The, 28
Seven Stanzas at Easter, 36
Shepherd Boy Sings in the
Valley of Humiliation, The,
205
Son and Father, 135
Song for Simeon, A, 202
Spacious Firmament on High,
The, 211
Sparrow's Skull, The, 141
Stone Angel, 11
Stone Too Can Pray, 177
Stranger, 14
Strong Son of God, 136
Sunday Morning, King's
Cambridge, 12
Theologians, 20
There Are No Gods, 70

There Was One I Met upon
the Road, 72
Third Enemy Speaks, 42
This World Is Not Conclusion,
10
Thou Art Indeed Just, Lord, If
I Contend, 88
Though the Great Waters Sleep,
91
Three Elements, 183
Three Helpers in Battle, 99
Thunderer, The, 109
To Destiny, 184
To the Sun, 21
Triumph of Doubt, The, 90
Tyger, The, 19
Up from the Bed of the River,
132
Village Atheist, The, 85
Way My Ideas Think Me, The,
54
We Are All Workmen, 56
We Shall Overcome, 165
What Are Years?, 138
What Though the Field Be
Lost? 76
What Will You Do, God,
When I Die? 55
When the Saints Go Marchin'
In, 97
When Wilt Thou Save the
People? 157
Windhover, The, 129
Wmffre the Sweep, 197
Yew Tree, The, 6
Zen Archer, The, 22

219

Index of First Lines

'A cold coming we had of it, 26

A mighty fortress is our God, 213

Above the voiceful windings of a river, 8

And death shall have no dominion, 60

And did those feet in ancient time, 162

And the Lord was not in the whirlwind, 154

Are You looking for us?, 163

As kingfishers catch fire, dragonflies draw flame, 134

At the round earth's imagined corners, blow, 58

Athirst in spirit, through the gloom, 98

Batter my heart, three person'd God, 52

Bear down lightly, 184

Beauteous, yea beauteous more than these, 97

Because I believe in the community of little children, 149

Bound to my heart as Ixion to the wheel, 144

Bowed by the weight of centuries he leans, 142

But God's own descent, 35

By reason of despair we set forth behind you, 102

By the glim of a midwinterish early morning, 135

Color—Caste—Denomination—, 159

Come out for a while and look from the outside in, 29

Comfort ye, comfort ye my people, saith your God, 175

Curse God and die, you said to me, 69

Doth some one say that there be gods above?, 70

Eastward I stand, mercies I beg, 173

Eternity's low voice, 122

File into yellow candlelight, fair choristers of King's, 12

For the second shot, 22

For them the sun shines ever in full might, 5

Forgive, O Lord, my little jokes on Thee, 40

Forgive us, O Lord, we acknowledge ourselves as type of the common man, 120

From gods of other men, fastidious heart, 83

Glory be to God for dappled things—, 124

God be in my head, 187

God is a proposition, 42

God, is, like, scissors, 50

God moves in a mysterious way, 210

God rest you, merry Innocents, 150

God's angry man, His crotchety scholar, 109

Going home by lamplight across Boston Common, 107

Good morning to you, Lord of the world!, 193

Have pity on us, Power just and severe, 182

Having been tenant long to a rich Lord, 44

He is the Way, 61

He, of his gentleness, 105

He that is down needs fear no fall, 205

He walks, the enchanter, on his sea of glass, 72

Here a little child I stand, 190

I am the pure lotus, 24

I ask you this, 172

I caught this morning's minion, 129

I had a beginning but shall have no end, 11

I have not been as Joshua when he fought, 99

I need no sky nor stars, 3

I struck the board, and cry'd, No more, 92

i thank You God for most this amazing, 195

I think continually of those who were truly great, 158

I warned the parents, you know, 33

I will bow and be simple, 188

I wonder as I wander, 204

If but some vengeful god would call to me, 65

If in that Syrian garden, ages slain, 87

If the red slayer thinks he slays, 23

In a dark time, the eye begins to see, 46

In the shadow of Old South Church the turn of spring is, 111

If there a cause why we should wake the dead?, 6

It's a great deal better to lose than to win, 74

Lead me, O God, and thou my Destiny, 185

Let nothing disturb thee, 178

Let us not look upon, 83

Life was a narrow lobby, dark, 201

Little boys and little maidens, 191

Little Lamb, who made thee?, 18

Little things, that run, and quail, 130

Lord, by whose breath all souls and seeds are living, 212

Lord, Lord—these miracles, the streets, all say, 177

Lord, the Roman hyacinths are blowing in bowls and, 202

Lord—Thine the Day, 188

Lord, Thou hast been our dwelling place in all generations, 198

Make me thy Spinning Wheel of use for thee, 49

Make no mistake: if He rose at all, 36

Mine eyes have seen the glory of the coming of the Lord, 160

Modest and needy is my destiny, in thy world, O God!, 192

My, fellowship, with, God, 50

My only son, more God's than mine, 31

My period had come for prayer, 171

My soul is weary of life; I will leave my complaint upon myself, 67

My Soul, there is a Countrie, 9

Myself when young did eagerly frequent, 66

No coward soul is mine, 4

Not all of them must suffer, 117

O beautiful for spacious skies, 164

O God, our help in ages past, 200

O love of God, God's love, love that alone, 181

O my deir hert, young Jesus sweit, 189

O potent Earth, and Heaven god-built, 180

O sing unto the Lord a new song, 194

O Thou my monster, Thou my guide, 179

O when the saints go marchin' in, 97

O world invisible, we view thee, 7

Of God we ask one favor, 71

Oh let your shining orb grow dim, 21

Oh Thou, who Man of baser Earth didst make, 40

Oh yet we trust that somehow good, 81

Old gods and goddesses who have lived so long, 13

On the sheep-cropped summit, under hot sun, 127

Our birth is but a sleep and a forgetting, 59

Our Father, 169

Our flesh was a battle-ground, 155

Out of the living word, 123

Poor soul, the center of my sinful earth, 53

Popcorn peanuts clams and gum, 152

Praise the good angel doubt, 80

Refusing to fall in love with God, he gave, 84

Return to the most human, nothing less, 116

Riding the black express from heaven to hell, 75

Saint Francis and Saint Benedight, 189

Say not the struggle naught availeth, 121

Shall I love God for causing me to be?, 45

So still the night swinging, 208

So zestfully canst thou sing?, 128

Strengthened to live, strengthened to die for medals and positioned victories?, 146

Strong Son of God, immortal Love, 136

Take as a gift, 47

Teresa was God's familiar, 108

The Angels came a-mustering, 100

The child is holy and most wise, 186

The churches, lord, all the dark churches, 86

The curé in his windy gown, 110

The earth is the Lord's, and the fulness thereof, 214

The Giver of Life, 25

The god would come, the god would go, 139

The kingdoms fall in sequence, like the waves on the shore, 141

The last and greatest Herald of Heaven's King, 106

The Lord of all, who reigned supreme, 199

The old priest Peter Gilligan, 114

The quietude of a soft wind, 41

The ribs and terrors in the whale, 207

The sea is calm tonight, 78

The Spacious Firmament on high, 211

The sun, God's eye, 91
The way my ideas think me, 54
The words of hymns abruptly
  plod, 196
There is much loveliness gone
  out of the world, 90
There was one I met upon the
  road, 72
They argued on till dead of
  night—, 20
They did not know this face,
  104
This ae night, this ae night, 139
This vast web, of Nature's
  weaving, 17
This World is not Conclusion,
  10
Thou art indeed just, Lord, if I
  contend, 88
Though the great Waters sleep,
  91
Three elements, 183
Thy need is great, 174
To fish for pearls in Lethe, 82
Turning and turning in the
  widening gyre, 28
'Twould ring the bells of
  Heaven, 131
Tyger! Tyger! burning bright, 19
Up from the bed of the river,
  132
Up to the bed by the window,
  where I be lyin', 176
We are all workmen: prentice,
  journeyman, 56

We shall overcome, 165
Wha kens on whatna
  Bethlehems, 156
What is our innocence?, 138
What shall we say it is to be
  forgiven?, 38
What though the field be lost?,
  76
What will you do, God, when I
  die?, 55
When all within is dark, 48
When God at first made man,
  51
When I look into the mountain
  air, 77
When I must come to you, O
  my God, I pray, 124
When Israel was in Egypt's
  land, 101
When Moses, musing in the
  desert, found, 57
When no one listens, 14
When wilt thou save the
  people?, 157
While you that in your sorrow
  disavow, 89
Whose little beast?, 126
Wilt thou forgive that sinne
  where I begunne, 206
Wmffre the sweep was mad as
  a mink, 197
Ye young debaters over the
  doctrine, 85
Yet if his majesty, our
  Soveraign lord, 16

ABOUT THE AUTHOR

Helen Plotz is deeply involved in awakening young people to an appreciation of poetry. Her three previous volumes—*Imagination's Other Place: Poems of Science and Mathematics*, *Untune the Sky: Poems of Music and the Dance*, and *Poems of Emily Dickinson*—have won her the respect and admiration of countless educators, librarians, and parents.

Mrs. Plotz was born in New York City and received an A.B. degree from Vassar College. For many years, she has served on the Children's Book Committee of the Child Study Association of America. The Plotz family considers travel its favorite hobby, and they have explored both the United States and Europe several times. Mrs. Plotz lives in Brooklyn, New York.

ABOUT THE ILLUSTRATOR

Clare Leighton is one of the most distinguished artists of our day. She was born in England and studied at the Slade School in London. Her first book was published in England when she was only seventeen years old.

She is a past vice-president of the National Institute of Arts and Letters and of the Society of American Graphic Arts, a fellow of the National Academy of Design, and a member of the Royal Society of Painters, Etchers, and Engravers in London. Her prints are displayed in museums both here and abroad.